INTRODUCTION TO CHILE

A CARTOON HISTORY

Chris Welch

Chile40YearsOn

First published in 1976 by Bolivar Publications
Reprinted in 2013 by Chile40YearsOn
Copyright © Chris Welch 1976

New foreword by Richard Gott
correspondent of the Guardian newspaper at the time who
witnessed the events before and after September 11, 1973 in Chile.

This book is being reprinted with the permission of the author and artist Chris Welch. It is a valuable historical document, both for its content and original mode of production. As a popular and accessible history of Chile up to the military coup of 9/11 1973, it is a useful part of the background to events in Latin America since then. In addition the collective way the book was produced in the Chile Solidarity Movement of the 1970's offers an example to us today. The further information page at the back of the book has been retained in its original form. For current information see www.chile40yearson.org

Reprinted by the Chile 40 Years On network in celebration of the achievements of the Chilean people under Salvador Allende, their courage in resisting the following Pinochet regime, and in memory of the victims and disappeared who suffered in the repression.

British Library Cataloguing-in-Publication Data. A catalogue record for this book is available from the British Library.

ISBN: 978-0-9926273-0-0

Sponsored and made possible by Unite the Union

HISTORY OF CHILE

by Richard Gott

The brief but brilliant moment evoked in the early 1970s by Salvador Allende and his Chilean Road to Socialism was rubbed out cruelly in September 1973 by the brutal coup d'état orchestrated by General Augusto Pinochet and the CIA, an event that led to a bleaker and far longer period in the history of Chile, characterised by murder and torture and, for thousands of people, the tragic experience of enforced exile. As a correspondent for the Guardian newspaper, I was witness to events both before and after September 11, 1973, and I saw the excitement of the Chilean experiment with socialism as well as the dark pain of the Pinochet years. These years are splendidly caught in the witty drawings and text of Chris Welch and his comrades in this cartoon History of Chile, first published in 1976.

The victory of Salvador Allende in 1970 was won almost by magic, with just 36 per cent of the vote. Allende had lost three earlier presidential elections and he only won on this occasion through a division between the country's right wing parties. His three years in power involved the gradual radicalisation of politics, with the nationalisation of many businesses large and small, and extensive land reform in the countryside. People on the left were in a state of permanent mobilisation, with land and factory seizures, and everyone involved in continual debate and dialogue. I remember travelling south to a land conflict with a French comrade and we were asked by the assembled peasants to explain what had happened to the revolution in our own countries. I was a bit shame-faced about the return of the British king in 1660, but my French friend talked happily about the execution of the aristocrats after 1789, and got the largest round of applause.

The right was not idle either, organising strikes and go-slows by the middle class and a devastating strike by lorry-drivers that paralysed the country from north to south. The CIA in the shadows, with the support of the US embassy and the foreign business community, was also active in sabotaging the economy, although many details did not emerge until later. Yet Allende's Popular Unity coalition remained popular throughout, securing as much as 43 per cent of the vote in the congressional elections of March 1973, a success that may have helped to promote the coup in September. The opposition and the Americans felt that there was now little chance of defeating Allende at the ballot box. A different strategy was needed. Dissident military officers were mobilised.

I flew into Santiago from Buenos Aires a week after the coup, in the first plane to cross into the country after the frontiers had been closed. The Aerolineas Argentinas plane had been chartered by Michael Brunson of ITN and John Humphrys of the BBC, and other journalists were welcomed aboard. We landed before dawn at 5 am and had to wait until the curfew ended. Santiago was absolutely silent at that hour and it remained so during the day. It felt like the silence of the grave. The beams in the presidential palace were still smouldering, and broken glass lay in the gutters in the streets around. The military had asked people to hang the Chilean flag from their windows in support of the coup, and there was not a house of a Socialist or a Communist where the owner did not think it politic not to do so.

I left Santiago and drove with a friend to the far south, to Temuco, to see what was happening outside the capital. We met troops on the road, and were stopped frequently by soldiers searching for guns. Everywhere we found small factories where the workers had been imprisoned or sacked. An atmosphere of fear enveloped the entire country. What had been a great socialist experiment was being rubbed out in a few weeks.

When I returned to Santiago, I found that almost everyone I knew was in hiding, waiting for the chance to dodge over an embassy wall. The British Embassy was firmly closed to visitors or possible refugees (Edward Heath was the British prime minister at the time), but other embassies were more obliging, notably Sweden, Holland, Panama and Mexico. Margaret Anstey, the UN representative, acted like a Flying Pimpernel, rescuing individuals and creating safe houses where the military were forbidden to penetrate.

Chile's loss was Britain's gain. When the Labour government returned to power in February 1974, Judith Hart was reappointed as the Minister for Overseas Development. She proceeded to divert British aid money destined for Chile to fund the efforts of the World University Service to sponsor Chilean academic refugees arriving in Britain; some 900 refugees were diverted to universities throughout the United Kingdom over a ten year period. An additional 2,000 non-academic refugees also came to Britain in those years, many of them trade unionists.

This large diaspora of Chilean leftists had an important and unforgettable impact on British political culture, bringing a wide range of music, dance, food and Marxist reading to inform and influence British political activism at a local level in the 1970s and 1980s. When other Latin American upheavals occurred in later years, notably in Nicaragua, Venezuela and Bolivia, a knowledgeable and internationalist audience had been created in Britain by the Chilean diaspora and its supporters. They were able to greet these new developments with encouragement and solidarity. Chile's years of trials and tribulation were to leave an unexpected and lasting impression on the British.

7

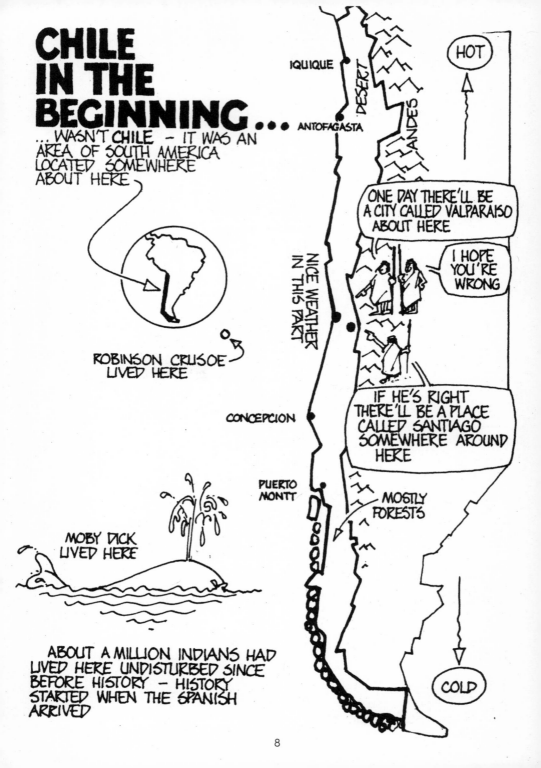

THERE WERE MANY DIFFERENT TRIBES OF INDIANS IN CHILE, SOME NOMADIC, SOME SETTLED - THEY LIVED BY FISHING, HUNTING AND FARMING
THE LARGEST TRIBE WERE THE **MAPUCHE** (MAPU = LAND, CHE = MAN)

THE INDIANS PLAYED A GAME, SIMILAR TO HOCKEY, CALLED "**CHUECA**" (ONLY THEY PLAYED THIS WITH STICKS AND A ROCK) ON THE WHOLE, LIFE WAS IDYLLIC

THE INDIANS FROM THIS PART OF SOUTH AMERICA HAD A LONG EGALITARIAN TRADITION - EVERYTHING WAS SHARED ; LAND, TOOLS AND WHAT THEY PRODUCED

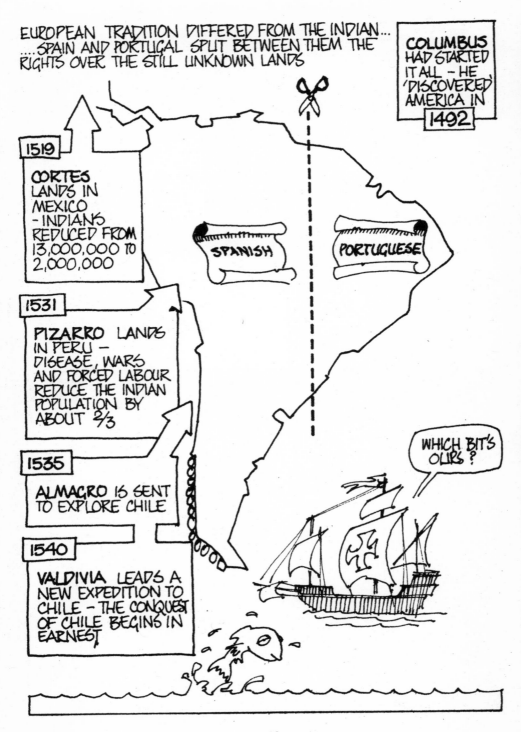

BUT THE SPANISH STAYED - THEY BELIEVED THERE WAS
SOMETHING WORTH STAYING FOR....

GOLD?

SO HUNGRY WERE THEY
FOR GOLD, AND SO DISDAINFUL
WERE THE INDIANS OF THIS HUNGER
THAT **VALDIVIA**, ONE OF
THE EARLIER CONQUISTADORES,
MET A RATHER NASTY END

!!

COME ON -
IF YOU'RE SO
HUNGRY FOR
GOLD -
EAT IT!

MMM...
MORE
SALT?

GRADUALLY SPANISH RULE WAS ESTABLISHED - FROM MILITARY
CAMPS AND FORTIFIED TOWNSHIPS - THE ORIGIN OF MOST
PRESENT DAY CHILEAN CITIES.

NOW THAT THE SPANISH HAD DECIDED TO STAY IN CHILE, CERTAIN ITEMS HAD TO BE DISTRIBUTED

.... AND, BY COINCIDENCE, PROVIDED A USEFUL LABOUR FORCE IN THE SEARCH FOR GOLD

HOWEVER, THE INDIAN SOCIAL STRUCTURE WAS PRETTY RESILIENT TO SPANISH EFFORTS TO SUBDUE IT, AND ALTHOUGH THE INDIANS WERE GRADUALLY FORCED SOUTHWARDS, THEIR RESISTANCE WAS TO LAST **3½ CENTURIES**

ALL WAS NOT LOST - THERE WAS STILL LAND (USEFUL FOR AGRICULTURE) - A FEW INDIANS AND....

THE MESTIZOS WERE A NEW TYPE OF CHILEAN A MIXTURE OF INDIAN AND SPANISH BLOOD.

TIME PASSED, AND AT THE OTHER END OF THE SOCIAL SCALE THE SPANISH AND INDIAN BLOOD HAD BEEN MIXING - PRODUCING AN ENTERPRISING INDIVIDUAL WITH SLIGHTLY DIFFERENT IDEAS FROM HIS SPANISH FOREFATHERS....

■ TRADE WAS LIMITED TO SPAIN AND SPANISH COLONIES
■ PLANTING VINES, TOBACCO, OLIVES, ETC. WAS FORBIDDEN
■ HEAVY TAXES WERE IMPOSED
■ CHILE'S ADMINISTRATION, ARMY AND CHURCH, WERE IN THE HANDS OF THE SPANIARDS (ONLY 20,000 OUT OF A POPULATION OF 650,000 BY 1800)
■ CHILE WAS CONTROLLED BY THE VICEROYALTY OF PERU WHICH IN TURN WAS CONTROLLED BY SPAIN (EACH TAKING ITS CUT)
■ ALL LITERATURE HAD TO BE SENT OFF FOR APPROVAL BY THE INQUISITION (RESULT: **NO** CHILEAN LITERATURE IN THE 17ᵀᴴ AND 18ᵀᴴ CENTURIES)

HMM... PERHAPS WE COULD DO WITH A LITTLE FREEDOM

PSST! DIEGO - HE IS THINKING ANARCHY

I SEE HIM PEDRO .... HE IS ALSO THINKING DIRTY FOREIGN THOUGHTS!

WE COULD SELL THINGS TO OTHER PEOPLE MAYBE

16

AS THE NEW IDENTITY OF CHILE DEVELOPED—AND WITH IT, QUITE NAT-
-URALLY, THE SPIRIT OF INDEPENDENCE—FRIENDS BEGAN TO APPEAR...
(...BUT DISCREETLY)

■ CONTRABAND TRADE HAD ALREADY STARTED BETWEEN CHILE
AND ENGLAND
■ NUMEROUS LATIN-AMERICANS WERE IN LONDON FROM 1785
ONWARDS, PLANNING THE LIBERATION OF AMERICA FROM SPAIN.
AT LEAST ONE RECEIVED A GRANT FROM THE BRITISH TREASURY
■ **WILLIAM PITT**, THE PRIME MINISTER, ALONG WITH OTHER ESTAB-
-LISHMENT FIGURES, SHOWED A GREAT INTEREST IN THE SPANISH
COLONIES
■ **LORD MELVILLE**, OF THE ROYAL NAVY, HAD REVIEWED A SCHEME
FOR THE LIBERATION OF SOUTH-AMERICA USING BRITISH NAVAL
SUPPORT

IN **1810** THE SOUTH-AMERICAN COLONIES STARTED DOWN THE ROAD
TO INDEPENDENCE

CHILEANS, ARGENTINANS, BOLIVIANS, VENEZUELANS AND
PERUVIANS ALL FOUGHT AS ONE, OFTEN IN JOINT ARMIES

IN 1810, CHILE'S FIRST INDEPENDENT GOVERNMENT WAS FORMED - SEVEN YEARS LATER ....

BERNARDO O'HIGGINS BECAME THE FIRST HEAD OF THE INDEPENDENT GOVERNMENT

DIEGO PORTALES FINALLY GAVE DEFINITE POLITICAL FORM TO THE NEW NATION - A STRONG CENTRALISED PRESIDENTIAL SYSTEM OF GOVERNMENT

D. PORTALES

AND AFTER INDEPENDENCE GUESS WHO SHOWED UP FIRST ?.....

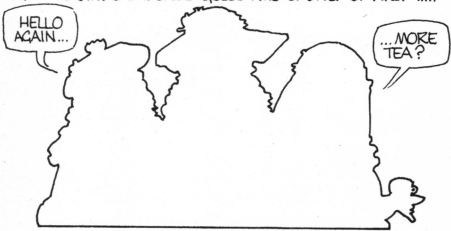

■ VALPARAISO - CHILE'S LEADING TRADE CENTRE - HAD A LARGE BRITISH COLONY AND CONDUCTED VIRTUALLY ALL BUSINESS IN THE ENGLISH LANGUAGE USING POUNDS STERLING
■ BRITISH INTERESTS SOON ESTABLISHED A LEADING POSITION IN SHIPPING, MINING, RAILWAYS AND FINANCE
■ TRADE WITH BRITAIN EXPANDED RAPIDLY, REPRESENTING OVER HALF OF ALL CHILE'S TRADE BETWEEN 1820 AND 1900

BRITISH INFLUENCE TOOK A GREAT STEP FORWARD DURING THE **WAR OF THE PACIFIC** - (1879-83), CHILE SEIZED CONTROL OF THE RICH NITRATE FIELDS FROM PERU AND BOLIVIA — (WITH A LITTLE HELP FROM HER FRIENDS)

." ONE SHOULDN'T SPEAK OF A CHILEAN/PERUVIAN WAR, BUT RATHER OF AN ENGLISH WAR AGAINST PERU WITH CHILE AS AN INSTRUMENT "

(U.S. SECRETARY OF STATE — JAMES BLAINE)

CHILE NOW HAD A GREAT NEW SOURCE OF WEALTH....

THAT'S NICE, - **WE'VE** GOT A GREAT NEW SOURCE OF WEALTH

Strikers in the stocks

■ JOHN NORTH AND OTHERS EMERGED FROM THE WAR OWNING MUCH OF "CHILE'S" NITRATES
■ OVER HALF THE MONEY RECEIVED FROM NITRATES NEVER SAW CHILEAN SOIL, AND VIRTUALLY NO NEW INVESTMENTS WERE MADE
■ **NORTH** CONSOLIDATED HIS HOLD ON NITRATES WITH MONOPOLIES IN THE REGION'S WATER, RAILWAYS.....

CONDITIONS FOR WORKERS IN THE NITRATE FIELDS WERE NOTORIOUS — EXTREMELY LONG WORKING HOURS AND STARVATION WAGES THAT WERE PAID IN CREDITS REDEEMABLE ONLY IN THE COMPANIES' STORES

FUGITIVES IN THE NITRATE AREAS GAVE ARMY OFFICERS THE EXCUSE TO INDULGE IN A SPORT CALLED "PALOMEO" (DOVE HUNTING)....

OBJECTIONS TO THE HARSH CONDITIONS WERE MERCILESSLY DEALT WITH ....

■ IN 1907 SOME 10,000 NITRATE WORKERS AND THEIR FAMILIES DEMONSTRATED IN THE NORTHERN PORT OF **IQUIQUE** TO TRY AND GET BETTER CONDITIONS — THE MILITARY WAS CALLED IN AND MACHINE-GUNNED THEM, KILLING **2,000** MEN, WOMEN AND CHILDREN.

CERTAIN SECTIONS OF SOCIETY DIDN'T LIKE HIS GOOD INTENTIONS.....

IN 1891 A REBEL 'GOVERNING JUNTA' WAS FORMED IN THE NORTH (WITH BACKING FROM THE NAVY AND OTHER MILITARY UNITS).

ACCORDING TO **THE TIMES** THIS NEW JUNTA IS "..MAINLY COMPOSED OF FRIENDS OF ENGLAND AND REPRESENTS ALL THE CONSERVATIVE AND WEALTHY ELEMENTS..."

THEY SOUND GOOD SORTS

CIVIL WAR RAGED FOR MANY MONTHS.

■ " IT IS WELL KNOWN THAT MANY BRITISH FIRMS HAVE MADE GENEROUS CONTRIBUTIONS TO REVOLUTIONARY FUNDS. AMONGST OTHERS IT IS OPENLY ADMITTED BY LEADERS OF THE CIVIL WAR THAT JOHN THOMAS NORTH CONTRIBUTED £100,000"(U.S. DIPLOMAT)
■ OVER 10,000 DIED
■ THERE WAS MASSIVE MATERIAL DAMAGE
■ BALMACEDA WAS DEFEATED AND COMMITTED SUICIDE

BALMACEDA DEPOSED!

I KNEW IT WAS TOO GOOD TO LAST

JUNTA INSTALLED

WITH BALMACEDA, ALL HOPES FOR INDEPENDENT CHILEAN DEVELOPEMENT DIED AS WELL.

SO THE WEALTHY SETTLED BACK INTO THE LIFE THEY ENJOYED — — IN SUMPTUOUS MANSIONS, FURNISHED WITH LUXURIOUS FRENCH AND VICTORIAN FURNITURE, DRESSED IN FINEST ENGLISH CLOTHES AND ITALIAN SILKS. JOURNIES TO EUROPE WERE FASHIONABLE.

WHAT WAS IT THAT **EDUARDO MATTE**, THAT BANKING CHAP, SAID THE OTHER DAY?

"WE ARE THE OWNERS OF CHILE, THE OWNERS OF CAPITAL AND LAND, THE REST ARE A MANIPULABLE AND SALEABLE MASS WHICH CARRIES NO WEIGHT, NEITHER IN ITS OPINIONS NOR PRESTIGE"

HOW DROLL

■ 1907 IMPORTS:
6,800,000 PESOS — CHAMPAGNE, JEWELS, SILK, PERFUMES
3,780,000 PESOS — AGRICULTURAL AND INDUSTRIAL MACHINERY

1890 GENERAL STRIKE
1898 FIRST MAY DAY CELEBRATIONS
1903 GENERAL STRIKE
1905 'RED WEEK' IN SANTIAGO
1909 WORKERS FEDERATION OF CHILE FORMED
1912 SOCIALIST WORKERS PARTY FORMED

BUT, AS YOU CAN SEE, WE WERE GETTING OURSELVES ORGANISED

DURING THIS PERIOD BRITISH INVESTMENT STOPPED GROWING AND CHILE FOUND SHE HAD OTHER VISITORS TO HER SHORES.....

HI! I'M J.R. THIS IS T.C. AND G.J. THAT'S K.L. AND T.J.....

...SWELL COUNTRY YA GOT HERE!

■ 1904-15 : MASSIVE COPPER MINING RIGHTS WERE SOLD TO THE U.S. – GUGGENHEIM AQUIRED CHUQUICAMATA, THE WORLD'S LARGEST OPEN COPPER MINE – THE BETHLEHEM STEEL CORPORATION GAINED A MONOPOLY OF CHILE'S IRON-ORE DEPOSITS – ANACONDA AND THE KENNECOTT COPPER CORPORATION ALSO MOVED IN.
■ FROM 1880 TO 1914 AMERICAN INVESTMENT HAD RISEN FROM 250 MILLION TO 1,700 MILLION DOLLARS.

POPULAR UNREST INCREASED – BETWEEN 1911 AND 1919 THERE WERE MORE THAN 300 STRIKES, AND IN 1919, 100,000 ATTENDED A MEETING TO FIGHT AGAINST RISING FOOD PRICES

FROM THIS TIME OF UNREST EMERGED **LUIS EMILIO RECABARREN**, THE FATHER OF CHILE'S LABOUR MOVEMENT.

■ AS A PRINTWORKER, HE HELPED SET UP MANY OF THE EARLY WORKING CLASS PAPERS.
■ HE WAS ACTIVE IN ORGANISING THE NITRATE WORKERS, WHO VOTED HIM INTO CONGRESS (WHERE HE WAS REFUSED A SEAT)
■ HE WAS A LEADING FIGURE IN THE **WORKERS** FEDERATION OF CHILE, WHICH HAD SOME 140,000 MEMBERS BY 1924.
■ HE FOUNDED AND LED THE **SOCIALIST WORKERS PARTY**, WHICH HAD A MASS WORKING CLASS BASE – THIS BECAME THE **CHILEAN COMMUNIST PARTY** IN 1922.

UP TILL NOW, CONGRESSIONAL SEATS ALL HAD MORE OR LESS FIXED AND PUBLICLY KNOWN PRICES — A LITTLE BOOZE AND A DAY OFF WORK HAD BEEN SUFFICIENT TO SECURE A SEAT....

BUT MASS DISCONTENT WAS PRESSURISING POLITICIANS TO PUT ON A MORE DEMOCRATIC FRONT.

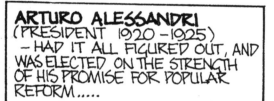

ARTURO ALESSANDRI (PRESIDENT 1920–1925) — HAD IT ALL FIGURED OUT, AND WAS ELECTED ON THE STRENGTH OF HIS PROMISE FOR POPULAR REFORM.....

...YOU'RE NOT GOING TO BELIEVE THIS BUT REFORMS GOT DELAYED...

..... AND THINGS GOT BACK TO NORMAL...

☐ 1921: **SAN GREGORIO MASSACRE** — THE ARMY REPRESSED STRIKING NITRATE WORKERS, KILLING OVER **100** — ALESSANDRI BACKED THE ARMY'S ACTIONS.
☐ 1925: **U.S. FINANCIAL MISSION** — U.S. 'EXPERTS' RECOMMENDED A PROGRAMME TO ATTRACT FOREIGN CAPITAL — ALESSANDRI COMPLIED.

25

BUT DAD... NONE OF THE OTHER KIDS PLAY CRICKET ANY MORE!

■ 1916 · FIRST NATIONAL CITY BANK (N.Y.) SETS UP SHOP
■ 1918 · W.R. GRACE SET UP MACHINERY BUSINESS
■ 1920 · DUPONT AND I.C.I. FOUND LATIN AMERICA'S BIGGEST EXPLOSIVES PLANT IN CHILE

NATURALLY THEY TOOK STEPS TO KEEP THINGS THIS WAY

■ CORRUPTION: POLITICIANS WERE BRIBED WITH ELECTION CONTRIBUTIONS, PLUM CONTRACTS, GIFTS, JOBS FOR RELATIVES. ETC...
■ PROPAGANDA: THE COMPANIES SPENT HEAVILY ON PROPAGANDA - LARGELY PAID FOR BY THE CHILEAN GOVERNMENT THROUGH TAX RELIEF
■ PRESSURE: SOMETIMES A HEAVIER HAND WAS NEEDED - THE U.S. SECRETARY OF STATE ONCE WARNED CHILE'S GOVT. AGAINST INTERVENING ON BEHALF OF STRIKING COPPER WORKERS AT KENNECOTT - "KENNECOTT'S 90,000 STOCKHOLDERS ARE NOT WITHOUT INFLUENCE'" - HE SAID, GOING ON TO THREATEN CHILE'S CREDIT SITUATION.

J.D., HOW CAN I THANK YOU FOR ALL YOU'VE DONE FOR MY NEPHEW?

WELL, NOW YOU COME TO MENTION IT....

MANAGER

THE AMERICANS' ATTITUDE TO THE CHILEAN WORKERS HAS ALWAYS BEEN - HOW SHOULD ONE PUT IT? - UNSYMPATHETIC?

" TOO MANY CONCESSIONS HAVE ALREADY BEEN MADE TO THE WORKERS IN THIS CORPORATION. WHAT THOSE GODDAM INDIANS REALLY WANT IS AN HONEST-TO-GOD GERMAN - A REAL GERMAN OFFICER TYPE WHO'LL SCREAM ATTENSHUN! AND MARCH THEM UP AND DOWN UNTIL THEY FAINT FROM EXHAUSTION!" ✳

✳ MR. FAHM - HEAD OF ANACONDA'S CHUQUICAMATA MINE

ALL WAS NOT WELL - GROWING POPULAR DISCONTENT WAS REPRESSED MORE SEVERELY AND THE MILITARY BECAME INCREASINGLY PROMINENT —

- **COLONEL IBÁÑEZ** WAS ELECTED UNOPPOSED AS PRESIDENT IN 1927 AND INSTITUTED A FURTHER WAVE OF REPRESSION AGAINST WORKERS' POLITICAL AND TRADE UNION ORGANISATIONS.

COULD THINGS GET WORSE?....

...YUP!.... CHILE, ARM IN ARM WITH THE U.S. WAS HEADING FOR THE GREAT DEPRESSION —
— SALES OF COPPER AND NITRATES COLLAPSED —
— UNEMPLOYMENT SOARED —
— WAGES FELL INCREASINGLY BEHIND THE PRICES OF BASIC GOODS.

♪ BUDDY CAN YOU SPARE A PESO? ♫

THE WORKERS' MOVEMENT INCREASED ITS ACTIVITIES....

■ 1931: GENERAL STRIKE — AS A RESULT IBANEZ WAS FORCED OUT
■ 1932: 'SOCIALIST REPUBLIC' — IT LASTED 12 DAYS
■ 1933: SOCIALIST PARTY FOUNDED — A MARXIST PARTY WITH A STRONG WORKING CLASS BASE

.... **ALESSANDRI** SHOWED UP AGAIN (1932-38) — HIS REPRESSIVE POLICIES, INCLUDING ARMING CIVILIAN **'WHITE GUARDS'** TO PUT DOWN STRIKES, LED TO THE FORMATION OF....

■ THE **POPULAR FRONT** OF MIDDLE-CLASS AND WORKING-CLASS PARTIES. THE FRONT WON THE 1938 PRESIDENTIAL ELECTIONS, BUT WAS CRIPPLED BY A CONSERVATIVE CONTROLLED CONGRESS.
■ HOWEVER THE FRONT FOUNDED **THE STATE DEVELOPEMENT CORPORATION** TO PROMOTE INDUSTRIALISATION AND ECONOMIC PLANNING.

BREAD! ROOF! CLOTHES!

INDUSTRIALISATION

THEN CAME THE WAR - FOLLOWED BY POST-WAR PROSPERITY....
..... FOR SOME

WHILST SOME PROGRESS WAS MADE BY THE CHILEAN WORKERS, UNEMPLOYMENT AND PRICES STILL ROSE

IN 1948 THE COMMUNIST PARTY WAS OUTLAWED UNDER "THE LAW FOR THE DEFENSE OF DEMOCRACY"

BUT WOMEN ACTUALLY GOT THE VOTE

...IT WASN'T UNTIL 1949 MIND YOU.. BUT WE ACTUALLY GOT IT!

BUT WE ALSO GOT IBÁÑEZ BACK IN '52!

■ AFTER IBÁÑEZ RETURNED TO POWER, PREDICTABLE GOVERN-MENT SYMPATHIES SWUNG FURTHER AWAY FROM THE WORKERS TOWARDS AMERICA. IBÁÑEZ INVITED U.S. ECONOMIC ADVISERS TO DRAW UP A BLUEPRINT FOR CHILE'S DEVELOPEMENT – THE COMMISSION RECOMMENDED REDUCTIONS IN SOCIAL SPENDING, LESS GOVERNMENT INTERVENTION IN THE ECONOMY AND MORE FOREIGN INVESTMENT.

■ U.S INTERESTS CONTROLLED ABOUT 90% OF CHILE'S COPPER, 85% OF HER NITRATES, 95% OF THE TELEPHONES, 65% OF THE MOVIES, AND MUCH, OR MOST, OF THE IRON, STEEL, CEMENT, ADVERTISING, OIL DISTRIBUTION, SALT, SULPHUR, TEXTILES, CHEMICALS FOODSTUFFS, CARS, TRUCKS, TYRES, EXPLOSIVES, PAINT, GLASS, PAPER RADIO, T.V., PHARMACEUTICALS, TRANSPORTATION, BANKS, MANAGEMENT, TOURISM, ACCOUNTING, ELECTRICITY, SHIPPING, DEODORANTS, SOAP, TOOTHPASTE, WELDING RODS, BOTTLE CAPS, MAGAZINES, SHIPBUILDING, PACKAGING, ETC., ETC., ETC...
    AS WELL AS THE AMERICANS THERE WERE THE GERMANS, ENGLISH, FRENCH, ITALIANS, JAPANESE, CANADIANS, DUTCH, BELGIANS, SWEDISH, BRAZILIANS, CZECHOSLOVAKIANS, DANES, LUXEMBOURGHIANS, SWISS, ARGENTINIANS........

■ OVER 60 YEARS, THE BIG FOUR U.S. MINING COMPANIES ALONE TOOK OUT OF CHILE SOME **10,800 MILLION DOLLARS** (THE ENTIRE NATIONAL WEALTH OF CHILE — ITS INDUSTRIES, CITIES, PORTS, ETC. — WAS ESTIMATED IN 1970 AS ONLY 10,500 MILLION DOLLARS)

■ U.S. DICTATED COPPER PRICES COST CHILE **$500 MILLION** DURING W.W.II AND **$300 MILLION** DURING THE KOREAN WAR.

■ UNDECLARED **ANACONDA** GOLD AND SILVER EXPORTS COST CHILE SOME **$40 MILLION**

■ IN 1968 ALONE, THE HUNDRED ODD U.S. COMPANIES OPERATING IN CHILE MADE **$700 MILLION** — EQUAL TO **12%** OF CHILE'S GROSS DOMESTIC PRODUCT.

THEY CAN'T DO THIS TO US!

THEY ALREADY DID

BUT...

.... IN 1959 THE **CUBAN REVOLUTION** ("FIRST FREE TERRITORY OF THE AMERICAS") PRODUCED A WAVE OF ENTHUSIASM ALL OVER LATIN-AMERICA.

MANY NEW POLITICAL MOVEMENTS EMERGED, BASED ON THE CUBAN EXPERIENCE....

... THE **MIR** IN CHILE, **ERP** IN ARGENTINA, **TUPAMAROS** IN URUGUAY, **ALN** IN BRAZIL, **ELN** IN COLOMBIA AND MANY OTHERS THROUGHOUT THE CONTINENT

THE U.S. REACTED BY IMPOSING A COMPLETE BLOCKADE ON CUBA AND AN INVASION WHICH DIDN'T QUITE WORK

... AND *STAY* OUT!

...OF COURSE, THE U.S. COULDN'T LET THE REST OF LATIN-AMERICA RUN AROUND WITH WILD IDEAS, SO THEY THOUGHT UP THE....

■ **ALLIANCE FOR PROGRESS** – LAUNCHED BY THE U.S. AS THE "ALTERNATIVE REVOLUTION" – OFFERING A PROGRAMME OF VERY MEAGRE REFORMS WHICH WERE HARDLY EVER IMPLE--MENTED

...RECOGNISING THAT NO REAL CHANGES WERE GOING TO HAPPEN, A SECOND FORM OF "ASSISTANCE" WAS INTRODUCED...

■ **THE MILITARY ASSISTANCE PROGRAMME**

AS THE U.S. ASSISTANT-SECRETARY OF STATE SAID – "THE CONTINUANCE OF INADEQUATE AND INEQUITABLE ECONOMIC AND SOCIAL STRUCTURES WHICH ARE VULNERABLE TO SUBVERSION, NECESSITATES THE MAINTENANCE OF THE COUNTER INSURGENCY CAPABILITIES OF LATIN--AMERICAN FORCES IN ORDER THAT AN INTERNAL ATMOSPHERE CONDUCIVE TO SOCIAL AND ECONOMIC PROGRESS CAN PREVAIL"

YOU KNOW, THAT'S WHAT I LIKE ABOUT THEM... ...ALWAYS READY TO HELP OUT!

I'VE NOTICED

YANKEE GO HOME!

THE CHRISTIAN DEMOCRAT PARTY, HEADED BY **EDUARDO FREI**, TOOK POWER. FREI WAS ELECTED PRESIDENT AFTER HAVING DEFEATED **SALVADOR ALLENDE** THROUGH A COALITION WITH THE RIGHT-WING PARTIES IN 1964.

EDUARDO FREI

DESPITE ONE OR TWO GOOD INTENTIONS, NOTHING REALLY CHANGED.....

■ **COPPER CHILEANISATION** (STATE ASSOCIATION WITH BIG COPPER CORPORATIONS) WHICH MEANT INCREASING KENNECOTT'S PROFITS BY 400% AND ANACONDA'S PROFITS BY 760%

■ A COPPER MINERS' STRIKE WAS BROKEN IN THE NORTH – THE ARMY KILLED 6 MINERS, 2 WOMEN AND LEFT SEVERAL DOZEN WOUNDED.

■ **PUERTO MONTT MASSACRE** – 200 GRUPO MOVIL (A SPECIAL POLICE FORCE) – ARMED WITH TEAR-GAS, RIFLES, MACHINE-GUNS AND PETROL - BURNED DOWN A PEACEFUL SQUATTERS' SETTLEMENT, KILLING 9 AND INJURING 30.

THE AGRARIAN SITUATION :

BEFORE FREI'S AGRARIAN REFORM THE LAND WAS MONOPOLISED BY A FEW BIG LANDOWNERS - AFTER FREI'S AGRARIAN REFORM THE LAND WAS MONOPOLISED BY ....

THINK I'LL PUT IN SOME POTATOES NEXT YEAR

MANY CHRISTIAN-DEMOCRATS GREW INCREASINGLY DISILLUSIONED WITH FREI — A CHRISTIAN-DEMOCRAT CONGRESSMAN SAID NEAR THE END OF FREI'S GOVERNMENT :–

" WE HAVE DONE VERY LITTLE FOR THAT 85% OF THE POPULATION WHICH VOTED FOR A REVOLUTION, WHILE WE ARE MAKING CONTINUAL CONCESSIONS TO AN OLIGARCHY AND A BUREAUCRATIC MINORITY OF 15% "

A NUMBER OF MEMBERS SPLIT FROM THE CHRISTIAN-DEMOCRAT PARTY TO FORM A NEW POLITICAL PARTY — THE **MAPU** (MOVEMENT FOR UNITED POPULAR ACTION)

■ THE CLASS CONFLICT GREW DRAMATICALLY :

PERIOD	No. OF STRIKES	No. OF STRIKERS
1965 - 1966	1,796	377,794
1967 - 1968	2,239	514,176
1969 - 1970	2,796	922,000

IN 1969 THE COMMUNISTS, SOCIALISTS, RADICALS, MAPU AND OTHER LEFT-WING PARTIES FORMED A COALITION KNOWN AS **POPULAR UNITY**

THEIR CANDIDATE FOR THE 1970 PRESIDENTIAL ELECTION WAS **SALVADOR ALLENDE** (ONE OF THE FOUNDERS OF THE SOCIALIST PARTY OF CHILE – AND THREE TIMES PRESIDENTIAL CANDIDATE)

HIS OPPONENTS WERE :-
JORGE ALESSANDRI – EXTREME RIGHT-WING INDEPENDENT (AND SON OF ARTURO ALESSANDRI)
RADOMIRO TOMIC – CHRISTIAN DEMOCRAT

NEARLY 18,000 "POPULAR UNITY COMMITTEES" WERE FORMED DURING THE ELECTION CAMPAIGN, BRINGING TOGETHER PARTY MILITANTS AND OTHERS SYMPATHETIC WITH THE P.U.

THE POPULAR UNITY PROGRAMME STATES THAT THE COMMITTEES WILL CONTINUE AS A MASS BASE FOR THE DEVELOPMENT OF POPULAR POWER

.... IN REALITY, THE COMMITTEES WERE ALLOWED TO VIRTUALLY DISAPPEAR

RIGHT WING PROPAGANDA COMPARED A POSSIBLE MARXIST GOVERNMENT WITH CUBA — A PLACE THEY WEREN'T TOO KEEN ON

SEE THE SIMILARITY? — JUST TAKE AWAY THE BEARD, THE CIGAR, THE HAT — SUBSTITUTE A PAIR OF GLASSES A MOUSTACHE? ...

... YOU NOTICE YOU NEVER SEE THEM AT THE SAME TIME IN THE SAME PLACE!

CASTRO

ALLENDE

THIS IS HOW THE ELECTIONS WENT ON **4 SEPTEMBER 1970** :

ALLENDE - 36·3%
ALESSANDRI - 34·9%
TOMIC - 27·4%

THAT'S IT! ... HE'S GOT THE MOST VOTES!

...BUT NOT AN OVERALL MAJORITY

■ ACCORDING TO THE CHILEAN CONSTITUTION, IF NONE OF THE CANDIDATES OBTAIN AN OVERALL MAJORITY, PARLIAMENT MUST CHOOSE BETWEEN THE TWO TOP RUNNERS (THIS TAKES PLACE TWO MONTHS AFTER THE ELECTIONS) — BY CUSTOM THE CANDIDATE WITH MOST VOTES HAS ALWAYS BEEN SELECTED

UP IN THE U.S. THEY WERE
GETTING WORRIED ABOUT THIS
CONSTITUTIONAL DETAIL

"I DON'T SEE WHY
WE NEED TO STAND
BY AND WATCH A
COUNTRY GO COMMUNIST
DUE TO THE
IRRESPONSIBILITY OF
ITS OWN PEOPLE"

(HENRY KISSINGER)

I.T.T., WITH ITS BIG STAKE IN CHILE WAS EVEN MORE WORRIED...

PERSONAL & CONFIDENTIAL

INTER-OFFICE MEMORANDUM

ITT WASHINGTON OFFICE
1707 L STREET, N.W.
WASHINGTON, D. C. 20036.

To: Mr. W. R. Merriam

From: J. D. Neal

Date: September 30, 1970

For the past several years the State Department has been pre-
dicting an upsurge of Marxism in Chile, and foresaw the culmination of
the threat in the September, 1970, elections. Knowing this, the U.S.
stepped up its AID program in an attempt to help Chile remain democratic.

The State Department and AID admitted in public congressional
hearings that, "Chile is a country of major U. S. assistance emphasis
because of its important political role in the Hemisphere." They
continued the hearing by saying the liberal U. S. loan policy to Chile
is justified because they were putting the money in there to fight Marxism.
However, now that its program failed to prevent Allende from winning the
election, the U. S. says, "This is a Chilean matter, thus, we must not
interfere!"

Why should the U. S. try to be so pious and sanctimonious in
September and October of 1970 when over the past few years it has been
pouring the taxpayers' money into Chile, admittedly to defeat Marxism.
Why can't the fight be continued now that the battle is in the homestretch,
and the enemy is more clearly identifiable?

SOME CHILEANS WERE ALSO FAR FROM HAPPY - JUST AFTER THE ELECTIONS RICH PEOPLE BEGAN LEAVING THE COUNTRY.

■ 22 OCTOBER 1970 THE COMMANDER-IN-CHIEF OF THE ARMY, **RENÉ SCHNEIDER**, WAS SHOT AND KILLED.

SCHNEIDER WAS A MILITARY LEADER COMMITTED TO NON-INTERVENTION IN THE POLITICAL PROCESS. HE WAS SHOT AND KILLED BY RIGHT-WING TERRORISTS WHO HAD HOPED TO KIDNAP HIM · AND PROVOKE A MILITARY COUP.

...IT WAS A CLASSIC COVER-UP JOB, NOBODY KNEW WHO WAS RESPONSIBLE.

THE CHRISTIAN DEMOCRATS, WHO HELD THE BALANCE OF POWER IN CONGRESS, REFUSED TO CONFIRM ALLENDE'S ELECTION UNLESS HE SIGNED *"DEMOCRATIC GUARANTEES"* SEVERELY RESTRICTING THE NORMAL CONSTITUTIONAL POWERS OF THE PRESIDENT — ALLENDE COULD NOT REMOVE ANY OFFICER OR CIVIL SERVANT FROM THEIR JOB.

WHILST ALLENDE'S POSITION WITHIN THE POLITICAL STRUCTURE WAS A VERY DELICATE ONE, THERE WAS NO DOUBT OF HIS POPULAR SUPPORT

ON 4TH NOVEMBER 1970 SALVADOR ALLENDE WAS INAUGURATED AS PRESIDENT

THE 'SECOND INDEPENDENCE'

... Y NACE EL HOMBRE NUEVO
(.... AND THE NEW MAN IS BORN)

" WE SPEAK OF A **SECOND INDEPENDENCE** - THE FIRST WAS WHEN WE DEFEATED COLONIALISM AND ACHIEVED POLITICAL INDEPENDENCE - NOW WE ARE STRUGGLING FOR OUR ECONOMIC INDEPENDENCE WHICH WILL LEAD TO FULL POLITICAL INDEPENDENCE , SOMETHING WHICH DEVELOPING COUNTRIES UNFORTUNATELY DO NOT ENJOY "

THE NEW GOVERNMENT MOVED QUICKLY TO SEIZE CONTROL OF THE FOREIGN AND NATIONAL MONOPOLIES - INCLUDING THE **CHUQUICAMATA MINE**, THE LARGEST OPEN CAST MINE IN THE WORLD

ON **11 JULY 1971** THE CONGRESS APPROVED UNANIMOUSLY OF THE NATIONALISATION OF THE BIG U.S. COPPER COMPANIES - FULL COMPENSATION WAS TO BE PAID, BASED ON BOOK VALUE AND **AFTER** DEDUCTING EXCESS PROFITS FROM 1955 TO 1970 — AN ACCOUNTING SYSTEM WHICH BECAME KNOWN AS THE **ALLENDE DOCTRINE**, A THREAT TO THE MULTINATIONALS THROUGHOUT THE THIRD WORLD.

PRIVATE BANKS, IRON, NITRATES, COAL, CARS AND MANY OTHER KEY SECTORS WERE PUT UNDER PUBLIC CONTROL

FOLLOWING REVELATIONS CONCERNING I.T.T.'S INTERFERENCE IN CHILE'S POLITICS, THE TELEPHONE SYSTEM THAT IT CONTROLLED WAS ALSO NATIONALISED.

THE GOVERNMENT ACTED QUICKLY TO GET CHILE'S STAGNANT ECONOMY MOVING AGAIN

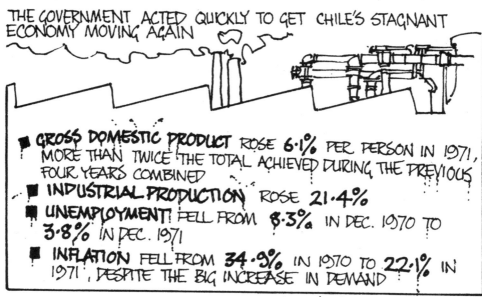

- **GROSS DOMESTIC PRODUCT** ROSE **6.1%** PER PERSON IN 1971, MORE THAN TWICE THE TOTAL ACHIEVED DURING THE PREVIOUS FOUR YEARS COMBINED
- **INDUSTRIAL PRODUCTION** ROSE **21.4%**
- **UNEMPLOYMENT** FELL FROM **8.3%** IN DEC. 1970 TO **3.8%** IN DEC. 1971
- **INFLATION** FELL FROM **34.9%** IN 1970 TO **22.1%** IN 1971, DESPITE THE BIG INCREASE IN DEMAND

MY POCKET MONEY WENT UP 15%

WHAT!...
..DON'T YOU REALIZE THAT REAL WAGES ROSE MORE THAN **20%** THIS YEAR!

..IT'S TIME WE UNIONISED!

PROFITS DID WELL FROM THE ECONOMIC BOOM, SO DID POPULAR UNITY – GETTING **49.7%** OF THE VOTE IN THE 1971 APRIL MUNICIPAL ELECTIONS

AGRARIAN REFORM

THE OPPOSITION-CONTROLLED CONGRESS WOULDN'T ALLOW A NEW AGRARIAN REFORM LAW TO BE PASSED, BUT THE GOVERNMENT GREATLY SPED UP THE APPLICATION OF THE OLD ONE

AND THE PEASANTS TOOK SOME INITIATIVES OF THEIR OWN....

SEEING AS HOW YOU'RE NOT USING THIS LAND, WE DECIDED TO PUT IT TO USE OUR-SELVES

OUTRAGEOUS! THIS LAND HAS BELONGED TO MY FAMILY SINCE THE FIRST CONQUISTADORS STOLE IT!

THAT'S RIGHT!

BY THE END OF 1972 THE LARGE ESTATES, WHICH EARLIER HAD CONTROLLED **65%** OF THE TOTAL LAND AREA OF THE COUNTRY, INCLUDING **80%** OF THE ARABLE LAND, HAD VIRTUALLY DISAPPEARED. CREDITS AND OTHER HELP — PREVIOUSLY MONOP-OLISED BY THE RICH — WERE MADE AVAILABLE TO POORER FARMERS

THE GOVERNMENT AND THE **C.U.T.** (T.U.C.) TOGETHER SET UP MECHANISMS FOR WORKER PARTICIPATION, WHICH WAS PARTICULARLY IMPORTANT IN FACTORIES TAKEN OVER BY THE GOVERNMENT — THE MAIN OBJECTIVES WERE:—

    (a) THE INVOLVEMENT OF WORKERS IN RUNNING THE FACTORIES
    (b) RAISING PRODUCTION LEVELS
    (c) DEFENDING THE FACTORIES AGAINST SABOTAGE

PARTICIPATION WASN'T AN AUTOMATIC THING — IT MEANT WORKERS TAKING THEIR OWN INITIATIVES AND AS THEY STARTED TAKING INITIATIVES, A LOT OF NEW IDEAS STARTED EMERGING

OF COURSE THE FUNCTIONING OF THE SCHEME WASN'T SIMPLE, IT CAME UP AGAINST A NUMBER OF PROBLEMS, INCLUDING THE INEXPERIENCE OF THE WORKERS AND THE BUREAUCRATIC HABITS OF MANY GOVERNMENT REPRESENTATIVES....

DESPITE THE MANY IMPORTANT SOCIAL AND ECONOMIC REFORMS CARRIED OUT, THE BASIC INSTITUTIONAL STRUCTURE OF THE STATE REMAINED UNCHANGED

THE "DEMOCRATIC GUARANTEES", SIGNED JUST AFTER THE ELECTIONS, STOOD IN THE WAY OF MANY ESSENTIAL CHANGES. AS WELL, THE GOVERNMENT FAILED TO IMPLEMENT ITS PLAN FOR A SINGLE "PEOPLE'S ASSEMBLY" - THIS WAS TO HAVE GROWN DIRECTLY OUT OF ELECTED LOCAL AND REGIONAL BODIES, AND WAS MEANT TO END REACTIONARY CONTROL OF PARLIAMENT AND THE JUDICIARY

ONE OF ALLENDE'S FIRST MOVES WAS TO DISBAND THE INFAMOUS 'GRUPO MOVIL', A SPECIAL U.S. TRAINED AND EQUIPPED POLICE UNIT, SET UP UNDER THE FREI GOVERNMENT...

A NEW USE WAS FOUND FOR THE WATER CANNON - ONCE USED FOR CROWD CONTROL, NOW....

CARLOS, OLD FRIEND, YOU DON'T THINK I'M CRAZY DO YOU?

COURSE NOT MATE

....WELL, THE POLICE CAME ROUND TO MY PLACE AND...

THE SWINE! WHAT DID THEY DO?

THEY WATERED MY GARDEN!! - I CAN'T TAKE IT ANY MORE!

RENT FOR HOUSING WAS FROZEN IN 1971, AND A LOT OF ENERGY WAS PUT INTO A NEW HOUSEBUILDING PROGRAMME AND HELPING SHANTY-TOWN DWELLERS TO BUILD THEIR OWN HOMES

OF COURSE, ENERGY WASN'T ALWAYS MATCHED BY SUPPLIES OF NAILS, CEMENT, WINDOWS...

..STILL, IT'S A BIG IMPROVEMENT

HOUSING:

■ "HALF A MILLION FAMILIES LACK HOUSING AND AS MANY MORE LIVE IN APPALLING CONDITIONS LACKING SEWAGE, DRINKING WATER, LIGHT AND HEALTHY CONDITIONS." — P.U.PROGRAMME.

IN 1970 ROUGHLY **HALF** OF CHILE'S CHILDREN WERE UNDERFED AND SOME **600,000** WERE MENTALLY RETARDED FOR LACK OF A PROPER DIET.

IF YOU DON'T DRINK YOUR MILK YOU'LL END UP LIKE THOSE 600,000

■ IN DECEMBER 1970 A **FREE MILK PROGRAMME** WAS STARTED — ALL CHILDREN UNDER 15 RECEIVED 1 PINT OF MILK DAILY

HEALTH...

TRADITIONALLY THE RICH AND MIDDLE-CLASSES WERE ABOUT THE ONLY PEOPLE WHO COULD AFFORD PROPER MEDICAL ATTENTION – THE POOR, ESPECIALLY THOSE WHO LIVED IN THE COUNTRYSIDE, USUALLY SUFFERED WITHOUT TREATMENT.

ALLENDE INCREASED HEALTH SPENDING AND SENT HEALTH TEAMS INTO THE COUNTRYSIDE AND ISOLATED DESERT AND MOUNTAIN AREAS, BRINGING FREE MEDICAL CARE AND DENTAL TREATMENT WHICH MANY HAD NEVER BEFORE ENJOYED

WOMEN'S RIGHTS
and CHILDREN'S RIGHTS

I GIVE IN ! I HAVEN'T HAD AN UNBURNT BOILED EGG SINCE MARIA WENT ON STRIKE !

- MAIDS WERE UNIONISED
- MATERNITY LEAVE WAS EXTENDED TO THREE MONTHS
- THE POPULAR UNITY PROGRAMME DECLARED THAT IT WOULD ESTABLISH ADEQUATE DIVORCE LEGISLATION – SAFEGUARDING WOMEN'S AND CHILDREN'S RIGHTS – AS WELL AS EQUAL LEGAL STATUS FOR ALL CHILDREN, WETHER BORN IN OR OUT OF WEDLOCK

EDUCASHUNTION

- POPULAR UNITY ALSO STATED THAT IT WOULD FIGHT FOR EDUCATION FOR ALL. THIS WOULD INCLUDE A GREATLY EXPANDED SYSTEM OF NURSERIES AND NURSERY SCHOOLS.
- ILLITERACY HAD BEEN A WIDESPREAD PROBLEM AND AN ADULT EDUCATION PROGRAMME WAS PUT INTO EFFECT....

.... SOME CASES WERE PARTICULARLY URGENT ....

HOW D'YOU LIKE THAT ? – THEY CALL FOR AN ELECTRICIAN AND THEN WON'T EVEN ANSWER THE DOOR !

OUT OF ORDER

CULTURE

"A NEW CULTURE CANNOT BE DECREED, IT WILL SPRING FROM THE STRUGGLE FOR FRATERNITY AS OPPOSED TO INDIVIDUALISM, FOR THE APPRECIATION RATHER THAN THE DISDAIN OF HUMAN LABOUR, FOR NATIONAL VALUES RATHER THAN CULTURAL COLONIZATION, AND FROM THE STRUGGLE OF THE POPULAR MASSES FOR ACCESS TO ART, LITERATURE AND THE COMMUNICATIONS MEDIA, AND THE END OF THEIR COMMERCIALIZATION"

DURING POPULAR UNITY, CHILEAN CULTURE FLOWERED

THERE WAS THEATRE AND MURAL PAINTING IN THE STREETS AND FACTORIES – AND EVEN A CULTURE TRAIN .....

CHANGES WERE ALSO MADE IN FOREIGN POLICIES — WITHIN 3 MONTHS THE GOVERNMENT HAD ESTABLISH DIPLOMATIC RELATIONS WITH **CUBA, NORTH VIETNAM, THE GERMAN DEMOCRATIC REPUBLIC** AND **THE PEOPLE'S REPUBLIC OF CHINA**

THOUSANDS OF POLITICAL REFUGEES CAME TO CHILE TO ESCAPE REPRESSIVE REGIMES IN BRAZIL, BOLIVIA AND OTHER LATIN AMERICAN COUNTRIES. THOUSANDS OF OTHERS VISITED FROM ALL OVER THE WORLD TO SEE CHILES "SOCIALIST EXPERIMENT".....

THE GROWTH AND DEVELOPEMENT OF THE POPULAR MOVEMENT LED INCREASING NUMBERS OF CHURCH PEOPLE TO COMMIT THEMSELVES TO THE STRUGGLE FOR A JUST SOCIETY

A NEW ORGANISATION, "CHRISTIANS FOR SOCIALISM", HELPED PROVIDE DISCUSSION AND COORDINATION FOR THOSE WHO CHOSE THIS LINE

THERE BEGAN TO EMERGE FROM THE HEART OF THE CHURCH VOICES AND WILLS DEMANDING A REAL COMMITMENT TO THE MESSAGE OF THE GOSPEL – GOD IS WITH THE POOR – THE POOR WANT SOCIALISM. CHRISTIAN LOVE PUSHES IN THIS DIRECTION, AND THUS, IN CHILE AND IN LATIN·AMERICA, SPRUNG FORTH **CHRISTIANS FOR SOCIALISM**. HUNDREDS OF PRIESTS AND THOUSANDS OF FAITHFULL WITHIN THE CHURCH PROCLAIMED THEIR DECISION THAT, WITHOUT FORMING AN ALTERNATIVE TO EXISTING WORKERS' ORGANISATIONS, THEY WERE WILLING, AS CHRISTIANS, TO MAKE THE GOSPEL AN INSTRUMENT AT THE SERVICE OF THE WORKERS

LONG LIVE SAINT KARL MARX!

■ IN 1971 THE **CHRISTIAN LEFT PARTY** WAS FORMED BY A NUMBER OF DISCONTENTED CHRISTIAN DEMOCRATS AND OTHERS

MEANWHILE....
...REACTIONARY FORCES
WERE FAR FROM IDLE...

94th Congress }
1st Session

COMMITTEE PRINT

COVERT ACTION IN CHILE
1963–1973

STAFF REPORT

OF THE

SELECT COMMITTEE
TO STUDY GOVERNMENTAL OPERAT[IONS]
WITH RESPECT TO
INTELLIGENCE ACTIVITIES
UNITED STATES SENATE

DECEMBER 18, 1975

Printed for the Use of the Select Committee [to Study Governmental]
Operations With Respect to Intel[ligence Activities]

U.S. GOVERNMENT PRINT[ING OFFICE]
WASHINGTON :

63-372

For sale by the Superintendent of Documents[, U.S. Government Printing Office]
Washington, D.C. 20402
Stock Number 052-0[...]

60

	1971—Continued
September 29	The Chilean government assumes operation of t[he] Chilean telephone company (CHITELCO). ITT h[as] owned 70 percent interest in the company since 193[0].
September 29	Nathaniel Davis replaces Edward Korry as U.S. Amba[s]sador to Chile.
October	ITT submits to White House an 18-point plan designed to assure that Allende "does not get through the crucial next six months." The ITT proposal is rejected.
November 5	40 Committee approves $815,000 support to opposition parties and to induce a split in the Popular Unity coalition.
December 1	The Christian Democratic and National Parties organize the "March of the Empty Pots" by women to protest food shortages.
December 15	40 Committee approves $160,000 to support two opposition candidates in January 1972 by-elections.

	1972
January 19	President Nixon issues a statement to clarify U.S. policy toward foreign expropriation of American interests. The President states that the United States expects compensation to be "prompt, adequate, and effective." The President warns that should compensation not be reasonable, new bilateral economic aid to the expropriating country might be terminated and the U.S. would withhold its support from loans under consideration in multilateral development banks.
April 11	40 Committee approves $965,000 for additional support to El Mercurio.
April 24	40 Committee approves $50,000 for an effort to splinter the Popular Unity coalition.
May 12	President Allende submits a constitutional amendment to the Chilean Congress for the expropriation of ITT's holdings in the Chilean telephone company.
June 16	40 Committee approves $46,500 to support a candidate in a Chilean by-election.
August 21	Allende declares a state of emergency in Santiago province after violence grows out of a one-day strike by most of the capital's shopkeepers.
September 21	40 Committee approves $24,000 to support an anti-Allende businessmen's organization.
October 10	The Confederation of Truck Owners calls a nationwide strike.
October 26	40 Committee approves $1,427,666 to support opposition political parties and private sector organizations in anticipation of March 1973 Congressional elections.
December 4	Speaking before the General Assembly of the United Nations, President Allende charges that Chile has been the "victim of serious aggression" and adds, "we have felt the effects of a large-scale external pressure against us."

	1973
February 12	40 Committee approves $200,000 to support opposition political parties in the Congressional elections.
March 4	In the Congressional elections, Allende's Popular Unity coalition wins 43.4 percent of the vote.
March 22	Talks between the U.S. and Chile on political and financial problems end in an impasse.

... THE U.S. AND MULTINATIONAL CORPORATIONS BEGAN A CAMPAIGN TO UNDERMINE THE ECONOMY —
— THE **INTER-AMERICAN DEVELOPMENT BANK**, THE **WORLD BANK** AND THE **CLUB** OF **PARIS** SUSPENDED MOST CREDITS AND LOANS, IN FACT ALMOST ALL CREDITS (INCLUDING BRITISH) WERE SUSPENDED.

BUT IT SAYS HERE THAT THE U.S. HAVE GRANTED A MILITARY CREDIT WORTH £ 2½ MILLION

HELPFUL!

CHILE'S DEPENDENCE ON COPPER EXPORTS WAS EXPLOITED THROUGH BOYCOTTS — MANOEUVRES WERE MADE TO ARTIFICIALLY LOWER COPPER PRICES — ATTEMPTS TO EMBARGO CHILEAN COPPER WERE TRIED IN SEVERAL EUROPEAN COUNTRIES. ONE ATTEMPTED EMBARGO BY KENNECOTT WAS MET BY ACTION FROM EUROPEAN DOCKERS

U.S. TECHNICIANS LEFT MINES, TAKING WITH THEM MAPS AND PLANS

SPARE PARTS SUDDENLY BECAME DIFFICULT TO OBTAIN

SO THE CHILEANS STARTED MAKING THEIR OWN PARTS....

LET'S PATENT IT BEFORE THEY START ASKING FOR ROYALTIES

CAPITAL WAS TAKEN OUT OF CHILE
AND FOREIGN INVESTMENT DROPPED
SHARPLY
SEVERAL CASES OF INDUSTRIAL SABOTAGE OCCURED

(THIS SCHOOL WAS SUPPORTED BY THE U.S. GOVERNMENT AND
THE BIG CORPORATIONS WITH INTERESTS IN LATIN-AMERICA -
SUCH AS ITT, KENNECOTT, UNITED FRUIT AND **W.R.GRACE**
-THE SCHOOL WAS ATTENDED NOT ONLY BY CHILEANS BUT
BY OTHER LATIN-AMERICANS AS WELL)

THE RIGHT LAUNCHED A HOARDING
CAMPAIGN AND RUMOURS OF
SHORTAGES, WHICH BECAME SELF-
FULFILLING BY ARTIFICIALLY
RAISING CONSUMPTION (DOUBLE
IN THE CASE OF SUGAR)

ON NOVEMBER 10 1971, **FIDEL CASTRO** ARRIVED IN CHILE FOR A 25-DAY VISIT — HIS FIRST TO ANOTHER LATIN-AMERICAN COUNTRY SINCE THE O.A.S. BOYCOTT ACTION WAS PUSHED THROUGH BY THE U.S. IN 1962

HAVING SUFFERED FROM THE SAME U.S. SABOTAGE AND HARRASSMENT THAT WAS NOW BEING TURNED AGAINST CHILE, HE BROUGHT A POWERFUL MESSAGE OF THE OBSTACLES TO BE FACED AND OF THE POSSIBILITY OF WINNING

IN CUBA WE DEFEATED OUR ENEMIES!

...IN CHILE WE'VE MANAGED TO CONFUSE OUR ENEMIES.. ...I THINK

ON DECEMBER 1, JUST BEFORE CASTRO LEFT, THE FIRST " **POTS AND PANS**" MARCH WAS ORGANISED. 5,000 WOMEN PROTESTED AGAINST THE CASTRO VISIT AND 'FOOD SHORTAGES'. IT WAS A TECHNIQUE HE HAD MET PERSONALLY SOME 10 YEARS EARLIER

IN OCTOBER 1972, THE RIGHT USED THE 'EXCUSE' OF OPPOSING A PLANNED PUBLIC LORRY TRANSPORT SYSTEM IN ONE SOUTHERN PROVINCE TO LAUNCH THE FAMED "BOSSES' STRIKE".... THAT IS, A MASS LOCK-OUT

THE **BOSSES' STRIKE** BROUGHT TO A HEAD THE RIGHT-WING TACTICS OF SABOTAGE AND SUBVERSION. THE IDEA WAS TO BRING THE COUNTRY TO A STANDSTILL AND THEREBY FORCE OUT THE GOVERNMENT

OCTOBER 9	LORRY OWNERS' STRIKE
OCTOBER 13	SHOP OWNERS DECLARE A NATIONAL STRIKE
OCTOBER 14	RIGHT-WING PARTIES DECLARE SUPPORT FOR THE STRIKERS
OCTOBER 17	THE DOCTORS' ASSOCIATION AND BUS-OWNERS JOIN IN
OCTOBER 19	STRIKE GENERALISED — BUSINESSMEN, INDUSTRIALISTS, PROFESIONALS, ETC. JOIN IN

THE 'STRIKE' CREATED MASSIVE ECONOMIC PROBLEMS — INDUSTRIES CLOSED, SUPPLIES AND SERVICES WERE CUT OFF, FARMERS OFTEN LACKED FERTILISERS AND OTHER ESSENTIAL MATERIALS THE STRIKE IS ESTIMATED TO HAVE COST BETWEEN $100 MILLION AND $200 MILLION

THE ATTACK FROM THE RIGHT TRIGGERED OFF A HUGE POPULAR RESPONSE LED BY THE ORGANISED WORKERS AND PEASANTS. MASS ORGANISATIONS WERE FORMED TO GUARANTEE THE FLOW OF PRODUCTION AND DISTRIBUTION
.... STUDENTS GAVE A HELPING HAND TOO....

IDLE LORRIES FACTORIES AND LAND WERE SEIZED, AND DOZENS OF NEW ORGANISATIONS WERE SET UP TO ADMINISTER THEM IN THE PUBLIC INTEREST

THIS POPULAR CONTROL RESULTED IN THE FORMATION OF "**INDUSTRIAL BELTS**" (INDUSTRIAL DISTRICTS ENTIRELY CONTROLLED BY WORKERS) — THESE WERE A BASIS FOR BUILDING COMMUNAL COUNCILS OF WORKERS, WHICH BROUGHT TOGETHER TRADE UNIONS, SELF-DEFENSE COMMITTEES, NEIGHBOURHOOD COUNCILS, MOTHERS' CENTRES, DISTRIBUTION COMMITTEES, PEASANT COMMITTEES, ETC. IN AN OVERALL CONTROLLING BODY FOR A WHOLE REGION

O.K. — THIS IS THE PLAN...

...THE CRATE OF APPLES WILL BE RELEASED BY THE FARM COMMITTEE, THE TRANSPORT COMMITTEE WILL TAKE IT ACROSS TOWN GUARDED BY THE SELF-DEFENSE COMMITTEE IT WILL THEN BE HANDED OVER TO THE DISTRIBUTION COMMITTEE WHO WILL LIAISE WITH THE ANTI BLACK-MARKET COMMITTEE BEFORE SENDING IT ON TO THE FARM COMMITTEE

I SEE... IT'S A **DECOY**?

NO... I THINK THE PLANNING COMMIT-TEE BLEW IT!

IT WAS THE WORKERS' CHANCE TO DISCOVER THEIR STRENGTH – TO DEFEAT THE RIGHT AND TO START BUILDING A REAL DEMOCRACY IN WHICH THE PEOPLE THEMSELVES WOULD HAVE THE FINAL SAY

POPULAR POWER, EXPRESSED CHIEFLY THROUGH THE INDUSTRIAL BELTS, WAS NOT JUST A WAY OF SUPPORTING THE GOVERNMENT; IT WAS A DIRECT TAKING OF POWER BY THE WORKERS FROM THE BOSSES

THE GOVERNMENT GAVE SOME HELP IN DEVELOPING THIS NEW 'POPULAR POWER' AND BROUGHT REPRESENTATIVES OF THE MILITARY INTO THE CABINET IN AN ATTEMPT TO STRENGTHEN ITS AUTHORITY. MANY RIGHT-WINGERS WELCOMED THIS DEVELOPMENT – UNTIL THEY REALISED THAT SOME REPRESENTATIVES (PRATS, BACHELET – BOTH LATER ASSASINATED) WERE ACTUALLY GOING TO CARRY OUT THE INSTRUCTIONS OF THE GOVERNMENT.

BY NOVEMBER 5TH THE "BOSSES' STRIKE" HAD BEEN DEFEATED – WORSE – IT HAD BACKFIRED BY FORCING A MAJOR LEFT-WING ADVANCE. MUCH OF WHAT THE PEOPLE HAD CREATED DURING THIS PERIOD WAS TO REMAIN INTACT DURING THE MONTHS THAT FOLLOWED

THE SECOND MAJOR DEFEAT FOR THE RIGHT CAME WITH THE PARLIAMENTARY ELECTIONS IN MARCH 1973 – DESPITE THE DEFEAT OF THEIR 'STRIKE' THE BOSSES FIGURED THAT CONTINUED SHORT-AGES AND CHAOS WOULD GIVE THEM A SUBSTANTIAL MAJORITY

– AS IT TURNED OUT, POPULAR UNITY TOOK **44%** OF THE VOTE (WHICH WAS 8% MORE THAN IN 1970, DESPITE ALL THE PROBLEMS ENCOUNTERED SINCE THEN)

THE RIGHT WAS REDUCED TO IT'S FINAL OPTION – **SOFOFA** (CHILE'S C.B.I.) HAD STATED THAT IF POPULAR UNITY GOT MORE THAN 40% OF THE VOTE, THE ONLY WAY OF GETTING RID OF THE GOVERNMENT WOULD BE BY FORCE

SURROUNDED BY MOUNTING CONFLICT AND CHAOS, AND CONSTANT RUMOURS OF A MILITARY COUP, DIFFERENT IDEAS ABOUT THE "CHILEAN ROAD TO SOCIALISM" WERE DEBATED WITH INCREASING CONCERN...

THE PROBLEM IS, WE'RE TRYING TO DO THINGS TOO QUICKLY

WHAT?! - IF WE DON'T GET THINGS DONE A LOT FASTER IT'S GOING TO BE TOO LATE

OUR ONLY HOPE IS TO KEEP STRICTLY TO THE CONSTITUTION..

BUT *THEY'RE* NOT KEEPING TO THE CONSTITUTION!.. AND THEY'RE PULLING STRINGS WITH THE MILITARY!!

YOU'RE WORRYING TOO MUCH — WE'VE GOT A *PROFESSIONAL* ARMY— THAT MEANS IT'S SUPPOSED TO OBEY THE GOVERNMENT

ANYWAY - GENERAL PRATS WOULDN'T LET ANYTHING HAPPEN

THE RIGHT INCREASED ITS ACTIVITIES

SABOTAGE, SHUTDOWNS IN KEY SECTORS, TERRORISM AND CONGRESSIONAL OBSTRUCTIONISM WERE ALL STEPPED UP.

PROMINENT IN THESE ACTIVITIES WAS "FATHERLAND AND FREEDOM" (**PATRIA Y LIBERTAD**), A FASCIST PARAMILITARY GROUP ORIGINALLY FORMED IN MARCH 1971.

THIS'LL GIVE YOU SOME IDEA OF WHAT THEY WERE LIKE....

Eight Methods for Overthrowing the Government

1. Unite in the face of the common enemy. (The Enemy is the UP and the Communist Party which directs it.)
2. Help to protect your local neighborhood.
3. Sabotage State-owned factories and work places.
4. Take justice into your own hands by directly punishing Leftist terrorists.
5. Denounce every irregularity in the enemies' behavior **only** to the Armed Forces.
6. Give your unconditional solidarity to the nationalist fighters.
7. Place resistance tasks above any personal interests.
8. Lend your solidarity to the working men and women who desire a clear destiny for the country. Act in coordination with the **gremios.**

On the reverse side the following message was written:

DON'T CONTINUE BEING A LITTLE SLAVE OF COMMUNISM. YOU DON'T DESERVE SUCH A VILE DESTINY. BE A MAN, BE A PATRIOT, SACRIFICE YOURSELF, REBEL, ACT TODAY. HE WHO IS A SLAVE WITHOUT WANTING TO BE ONE IS A COLLABORATIONIST. FIGHT TO CONQUER OR DIE.

At the foot of the leaflet, which was passed out by the thousands starting in mid-1973, is the insignia of **Patria y Libertad.**

A SUBSTANTIAL PART OF THE **EL TENIENTE** MINE WENT ON STRIKE — THE RIGHT BACKED THE STRIKE, USING THE OPPORTUNITY AS A FRONT FOR ATTACKING THE GOVERNMENT

WE'RE WITH YOU

BROTHERS

THEY MUST BE PUTTING US ON !?

DESPITE ATTEMPTS TO STRENGTHEN POPULAR CONTROL OVER PRICES, PRODUCTION AND DISTRIBUTION, PRODUCTION SUFFERED AND GOODS BECAME HARDER TO OBTAIN.

PRICES ROSE, AND A BLACK-MARKET GREW TO EVADE GOVERNMENT PRICE CONTROLS — SOME TOOK ADVANTAGE OF THE QUEUING FEVER

THE U.S. TOUGHENED ITS LINE ON CHILE'S REQUEST TO RENEGOTIATE ITS DEBT AND TALKS BROKE DOWN.

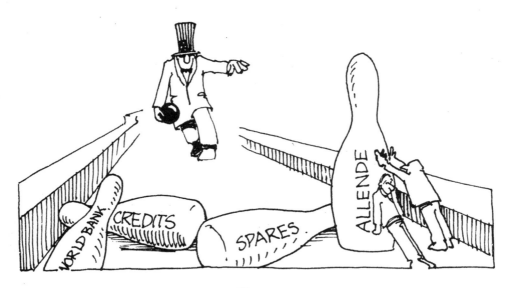

■ **TANCAZO** : ON JUNE 29TH AN ARMOURED TANK REGIMENT ATTACKED THE PRESIDENTIAL PALACE

FORTUNATELY THE ATTACK WAS BADLY PREPARED —
— SOME OF THE TANKS RAN OUT OF FUEL

WHAT DO YOU MEAN SERGEANT? YOU DIDN'T BRING YOUR WALLET!

GENERAL PRATS LED THE FORCES WHICH PUT DOWN THE ATTEMPTED COUP

THE PEOPLE TOOK TO THE STREETS IN A MASSIVE DEMONSTRATION THAT EVENING IN SUPPORT OF ALLENDE, AND MANY FACTORIES WERE TAKEN OVER BY WORKERS

CALLS TO GET RID OF REACTIONARY OFFICERS INCREASED, BUT THE 1970 "DEMOCRATIC GUARANTEES" WERE KEPT TO AND THE MILITARY HIERARCHIES LEFT UNTOUCHED....

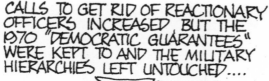

THE FASCISTS WON'T GET PAST US

... ONE FACT WAS EVIDENT - THE PEOPLE WERE UNPREPARED FOR A MILITARY CONFLICT.

AND IF THEY DO ....

... WE WON'T SALUTE THEM !

SEEING ITS STRENGTH, THE RIGHT PREPARED FOR ITS FINAL ATTACK

■ CHRISTIAN DEMOCRATS, FOLLOWING THEIR LEADER EDUARDO FREI, DECLARED THEIR TOTAL HOSTILITY TO THE POPULAR UNITY GOVERNMENT
■ LORRY OWNERS WENT ON STRIKE AGAIN, SOON FOLLOWED BY OTHER GROUPS (THIS TIME THE MILITARY GAVE NO COOPERATION TO THE GOVERNMENT)
■ ALLENDE'S NAVAL AIDE-DE-CAMP WAS ASSASSINATED AND A WIDESPREAD CAMPAIGN OF TERROR AND SABOTAGE AGAINST BRIDGES, OIL SUPPLIES, ELECTRICITY PYLONS, ETC. WAS LAUNCHED BY THE RIGHT

■ ON 23ʳᵈ AUGUST GENERAL PRATS WAS FORCED BY FELLOW OFFICERS TO RETIRE AS MINISTER OF DEFENSE AND COMMANDER-IN-CHIEF OF THE ARMED FORCES

ON JULY 8ᵀᴴ THE MILITARY STARTED MASSIVE RAIDS ON FACTORIES AND WORKERS' QUARTERS LOOKING (UNSUCCES-SFULLY) FOR "EXTREMIST" ARMS STORES – THEY IGNORED MOUNTING PREPARATIONS IN OTHER QUARTERS

■ ON AUGUST 5TH 1973 MORE THAN 100 SAILORS WERE ARRESTED ON CHARGES OF PLOTTING A MUTINY

READY FOR THE COUP?

SI SEÑOR!

WE'LL HAVE TO DO SOMETHING ABOUT THIS!

THEIR CRIME: OPPOSING PLANS FOR A COUP WHICH THEY DISCOVERED BEING DRAWN UP

THEY WERE SAVAGELY TREATED BY THEIR CAPTORS — AS THEY RECOUNTED IN AN OPEN LETTER TO THE CHILEAN WORKERS AND PRESIDENT ALLENDE...

"..... WE, THE RANK AND FILE SAILORS, WHO ARE OPPOSED TO A COUP, DECLARE TO THE WORKERS AND TO OUR FAMILIES THAT NEITHER THE THREATS OF OUR OFFICERS TO RETURN AND BEAT US AGAIN, NOR A THOUSAND FURTHER TORTURES WILL PREVENT US FROM TELLING THE TRUTH TO OUR CLASS, THE WORKING CLASS..."

THERE WAS A GREAT PUBLIC OUTCRY TO HAVE THE SAILORS RELEASED — THE GOVERNMENT FAILED TO ACT — THE "PEOPLE'S SAILORS" ARE STILL IN PRISON, AND HAVE BEEN TORTURED AND BRUTALISED AS A LESSON TO OTHERS WHO MIGHT THINK TO DISOBEY ORDERS

KISSINGER REGARDED CHILE AS SETTING A DANGEROUS PRECEDENT FOR ITALY, FRANCE AND ELSEWHERE, AND TREATED CHILE AS A TEST CASE FOR A SET OF TECHNIQUES WHICH HAVE BECOME KNOWN AS **DESTABILISATION**

WILLIAM COLBY (THEN DIRECTOR OF THE C.I.A) DESCRIBED CHILE AS A PROTOTYPE OR LABORA--TORY EXPERIMENT TO TEST THE TECHNIQUES OF HEAVY FINANCIAL INVESTMENT IN AN EFFORT TO BRING DOWN A GOVERNMENT" (TESTIMONY TO A U.S. CONGRESSIONAL COMMITTEE ON APRIL 22 1975)

■ OVER $8 MILLION WAS MADE AVAILABLE FOR SECRET MEDDLING IN CHILEAN POLITICS BETWEEN 1970-73

THE U.S. NAVY HAD AN ACTIVE ROLE IN HELPING CARRY OUT THE COUP ITSELF — THROUGH THEIR PRESENCE IN A JOINT NAVAL EXERCISE BETWEEN U.S. AND CHILEAN NAVIES AND THE U.S. NAVAL MISSION IN VALPARAISO, THEY PROVIDED SUPPORT AND LIAISON FACILITIES

THE MILITARY ALREADY HAD CONTROL IN SOME PROVINCIAL AREAS TWO WEEKS BEFORE THE COUP.

ON THE MORNING OF 11TH SEPTEMBER 1973 THE CAREFULLY LAID COUP PLANS WENT INTO EFFECT – THE PRESIDENTIAL PALACE WAS SURROUNDED – PRESIDENT ALLENDE AND THOSE WITH HIM REFUSED TO SURRENDER

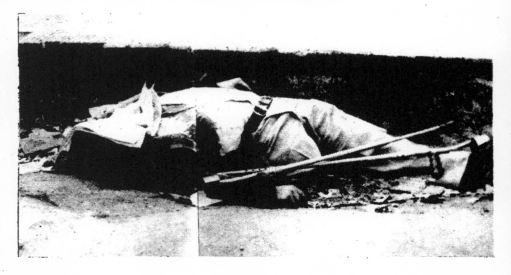

"..... WORKERS OF MY COUNTRY: I HAVE FAITH IN CHILE AND ITS DESTINY. OTHER CHILEANS WILL COME. IN THESE DARK AND BITTER MOMENTS, WHERE TREACHERY CLAIMS TO IMPOSE ITSELF, YOU MUST KNOW THAT SOONER OR LATER, AND VERY SOON, LARGE AVENUES WILL OPEN AGAIN FOR MEN WORTHY OF BUILDING A NEW SOCIETY.
LONG LIVE CHILE!
LONG LIVE THE PEOPLE!
LONG LIVE THE WORKERS!
THESE ARE MY LAST WORDS AND I AM CERTAIN THAT MY SACRIFICE WILL NOT BE IN VAIN. I AM CERTAIN IT WILL BE A MORAL LESSON WHICH WILL CONDEMN DISLOYALTY, COWARDICE AND TREACHERY"

(SALVADOR ALLENDE)

..... THEY WERE KILLED IN THE BATTLE AGAINST HAWKER-HUNTER JETS, TANKS AND TROOPS (THE MONEDA PALACE WAS LEFT IN RUINS)
THOUSANDS OF CIVILIANS WERE KILLED.

A MILITARY JUNTA, CONSISTING OF THE HEADS OF THE ARMY, NAVY, AIRFORCE AND POLICE DECLARED ITSELF THE NEW GOVERNMENT — A STATE OF INTERNAL WAR WAS DECLARED, MARTIAL LAW IMPOSED AND ALL INTERNATIONAL TRANSPORT AND COMMUNICATIONS CUT FOR A WEEK. A CURFEW WAS ENFORCED (IT STILL REMAINS TODAY)

THE PUBLIC RELATIONS MACHINE GEARED FOR EXTERNAL CONSUMPTION WAS ALL READY AND WENT SWIFTLY INTO ACTION

LEADING RIGHT-WINGERS PROCLAIMED WHAT A GREAT PATRIOTIC AND DEMOCRATIC DEED HAD BEEN DONE

THE MILITARY JUNTA SET OUT TO SYSTEMATICALLY DESTROY THE
POPULAR MOVEMENT AND THE GAINS THIS MOVEMENT HAD
ACHIEVED.

ALL CENTRES OF POPULAR ORGANIZATION WERE STORMED AND
KNOWN ACTIVISTS ARRESTED AND OFTEN KILLED. DESPITE
LACK OF PREPARATION (BOTH ORGANIZATIONALLY AND IN
LACK OF ARMS) SOME STRONG RESISTANCE TOOK PLACE.

CALL IN
THE
AIRFORCE

■ AT THE SUMAR TEXTILE
FACTORY MORE THAN 500
WORKERS DIED.
■ PANGUIPULLI FORESTRY
COMPLEX WAS BOMBED WITH
NAPALM.
■ FROM THE SHANTY TOWNS
SHOOTING WAS HEARD FOR
A NUMBER OF DAYS AFTER
THE COUP.

EVERY MORNING, IN SANTIAGO, CORPSES COULD BE SEEN
FLOATING DOWN THE RIVER. MANY MORE PILED UP IN
HOSPITALS OR WERE SIMPLY LEFT WHERE THEY FELL.

U.S. GOVERNMENT SOURCES
ESTIMATED THAT BETWEEN
10,000 AND 40,000 PEOPLE
WERE KILLED DURING THE
FIRST FEW MONTHS OF
MILITARY RULE. THE JUNTA
LATER TOLD THE UNITED
NATIONS THAT **ONLY**
30,000 WERE KILLED

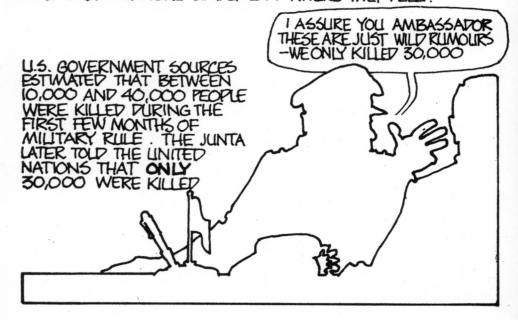

I ASSURE YOU AMBASSADOR
THESE ARE JUST WILD RUMOURS
—WE ONLY KILLED 30,000

MASSIVE ROUNDUPS AND DETENTIONS TOOK PLACE AND HAVE CONTINUED EVER SINCE.

■ SOME 10,000 WERE PUT IN THE NATIONAL STADIUM DURING THE FIRST FEW DAYS OF THE COUP.
■ MANY MORE WERE PUT IN THE CHILE STADIUM AND OTHER DETENTION CENTRES.
■ SINCE THEN, OFFICIAL REPORTS HAVE OFTEN STATED THAT THOUSANDS OF "DELINQUENTS" HAVE BEEN ARRESTED IN SINGLE WEEKENDS.
■ PERHAPS 150,000 PEOPLE HAVE PASSED THROUGH THE JUNTA'S GAOLS.

DECREE LAW Nº 23‍55

ALL ELEPHANTS FOUND IN SANTIAGO AFTER 12 NOON, WILL BE SHOT ON SIGHT.

IT'S 11·30 ALREADY!

I'D BETTER GET RUNNING!

THEY SHOOTING RABBITS AS WELL AS ELEPHANTS?!

NO..

...BUT I WOULDN'T TRUST THEM TO TELL THE DIFFERENCE!!

TORTURE WAS A STANDARD PRACTICE FROM THE BEGINNING. FOREIGN "TECHNICIANS", MOSTLY BRAZILIANS, HELPED IN OBTAINING CONFESSIONS AND INFORMATION

WANTED

"FOREIGN TECHNICIANS"

INTERESTED WORK CHIL

FOREIGNERS, MANY OF WHOM HAD FLED REPRESSIVE GOVERNMENTS ELSEWHERE IN LATIN AMERICA, BECAME A SPECIAL TARGET FOR THE CAMPAIGN OF TERROR.

THE LEFT WING POLITICAL PARTIES WERE OUTLAWED, AND ALL OTHER PARTIES DECLARED "IN RECESS"

HUNDREDS OF THOUSANDS LOST THEIR JOBS FOR POLITICAL REASONS. THE ELECTORAL ROLLS WERE DESTROYED AND GENERAL PINOCHET ANNOUNCED THAT THE JUNTA WOULD STAY IN POWER "UNTIL A NEW GENERATION IS FORMED"

THE **CUT** (CHILE'S TUC) WAS BANNED, AND ALL TRADE UNION BODIES THOROUGHLY PURGED AND "RESTRUCTURED"

- STRIKERS FACE SUMMARY EXECUTION.
- UNION ELECTIONS ARE FORBIDDEN.
- UNION PROPERTY HAS OFTEN BEEN CONFISCATED.

IN FACT ALL SORTS OF MOVEMENTS ARE BEING PERSECUTED....

AND THIS SEISMIC MOVEMENT THAT WAS REPORTED! — *I WANT IT STAMPED OUT !!*

ECONOMIC REPRESSION, TO REVERSE THE GAINS OF THE WORKERS AND RESTORE CORPORATE PROFITS, WAS AN INTEGRAL PART OF THE JUNTA'S PROGRAMME

■ MOST PRICE CONTROLS WERE RELEASED, AND IN THE FIRST TWO YEARS PRICES OFFICIALLY ROSE BY WELL OVER 3,000%
■ REAL WAGES HAVE FALLEN BY OVER 50%
■ UNEMPLOYMENT ROSE FROM 3.1% IN JUNE 1973 TO 18.7% IN DECEMBER 1975 (ACCORDING TO UNIVERSITY OF CHILE FIGURES) THE REAL FIGURE IS WIDELY THOUGHT TO BE BETWEEN 25% – 30%

"TEMPORARY" AUSTERITY MEASURES HAVE BECOME INCREASING--LY PROLONGED AND SEVERE. "NON-TRADITIONAL EXPORTS" – (FOOD, SHOES AND OTHER THINGS THAT CHILEANS DESPERATELY NEED BUT CAN NO LONGER AFFORD) – ARE BEING SHIPPED ABROAD IN MASSIVE QUANTITIES TO HELP COVER THE JUNTA'S DESPERATE BALANCE OF PAYMENTS PROBLEMS.

"CHILEANS MUST PUT AN END TO THE OVER-CONSUMPTION OF SHOES"
– ECONOMICS MINISTER FERNANDO LENIZ (SINCE REPLACED BY A "HARD-LINER")

GOVERNMENT SPENDING WAS TO BE REDUCED TO "BARE ESSENTIALS"

SPENDING ON SOCIAL SERVICES FELL BY 70%, WHILE MILITARY SPENDING TREBLED TO OVER 20% OF ALL GOVERNMENT SPENDING (INDIRECT MILITARY SPENDING COULD BRING THAT FIGURE TO 40%)

SOCIAL SERVICES LIKE HEALTH AND EDUCATION ARE BEING ORGANIZED ALONG COMMERCIAL LINES, SO THAT THE POOR CAN NO LONGER AFFORD THEM — CUTBACKS ARE FORCING MANY DOCTORS AND TEACHERS TO MOVE ABROAD.

THE ONE "FREEDOM" THE JUNTA DOES UNDERSTAND IS "FREE ENTERPRISE" — HUNDREDS OF STATE AND WORKER-CONTROLLED ENTREPRISES HAVE BEEN SOLD DIRT CHEAP TO PRIVATE (INCLUDING FOREIGN) INTERESTS WHILE THE BIG MONOPOLIES HAVE BEEN BUYING UP ALL THEIR SMALLER COMPETITORS.

I'VE GOT 5 SCHOOLS, 3 HOSPITALS AND 2 UNIVERSITIES ON THAT SQUARE...

..LET ME SEE — THAT'LL COST...

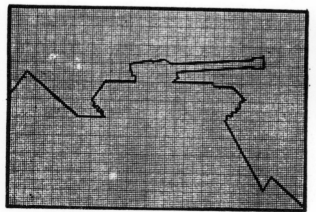

BUT THINGS HAVE BEEN GETTING SO BAD THAT EVEN THE BIGGEST INTERESTS ARE STARTING TO HURT — INDUSTRIAL PRODUCTION FELL 35% IN TWO YEARS

THE JUNTA'S ECONOMIC PLAN - DRAWN UP WITH THE HELP OF THE C.I.A. AND ADMINISTERED BY THE "CHICAGO BOYS" - INVOLVED OPENING UP CHILE TO MASSIVE FOREIGN PENETRATION. SOME $500 MILLION WERE PAID TO U.S. COMPANIES, LEGALLY TAKEN OVER DURING POPULAR UNITY, AND GENEROUS CONCESSIONS OFFERED.

DESPITE THE INDUCEMENTS, VIRTUALLY ALL FOREIGN INVESTMENT HAS BEEN SCARED OFF BY DOMESTIC ECONOMIC CHAOS AND DEPRESSION AND FEARS OF THE JUNTA'S INSTABILITY

O.K.! YOU GET THE PICTURE? - IF INFLATION MOVES - - SHOOT IT DOWN!

THE COUNTRYSIDE WAS NOT FORGOTTEN EITHER...

I'VE HEARD THAT THE CHINESE USE HUMAN EXCREMENT AS A FERTILIZER

■ MUCH OF THE LAND DISTRIBUTED UNDER ALLENDE, AND EVEN UNDER FREI, WAS HANDED BACK TO THE ORIGINAL OWNERS OR SOLD OFF TO THOSE WHO HAD THE MONEY.
■ THE OLD AGRARIAN REFORM INSTITUTIONS HAVE MOSTLY BEEN DISMANTLED.
■ PRICE CONTROLS ON FERTILIZERS ETC. WERE LIFTED.
■ THE WHEAT CROP FELL FROM A YEARLY AVERAGE OF 1,103,000 TONNES UNDER POPULAR UNITY TO ONLY 600,000 TONNES IN 1975

..EVEN THAT HAS BECOME SCARCE THESE DAYS!

THE EDUCATIONAL SYSTEM HAS BEEN RECAST FOR THE BUILDING OF A "GREAT CHILE"

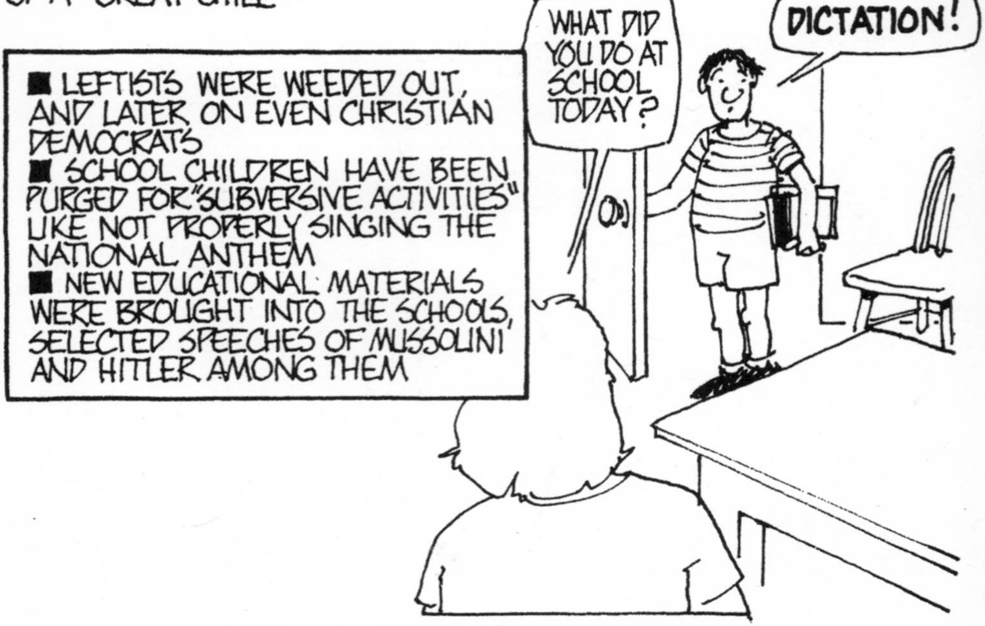

- LEFTISTS WERE WEEDED OUT, AND LATER ON EVEN CHRISTIAN DEMOCRATS
- SCHOOL CHILDREN HAVE BEEN PURGED FOR "SUBVERSIVE ACTIVITIES" LIKE NOT PROPERLY SINGING THE NATIONAL ANTHEM
- NEW EDUCATIONAL MATERIALS WERE BROUGHT INTO THE SCHOOLS, SELECTED SPEECHES OF MUSSOLINI AND HITLER AMONG THEM

WHAT DID YOU DO AT SCHOOL TODAY?

DICTATION!

THOUSANDS OF BOOKS WERE BURNED IN AN EFFORT TO STAMP OUT "MARXIST PROPAGANDA"

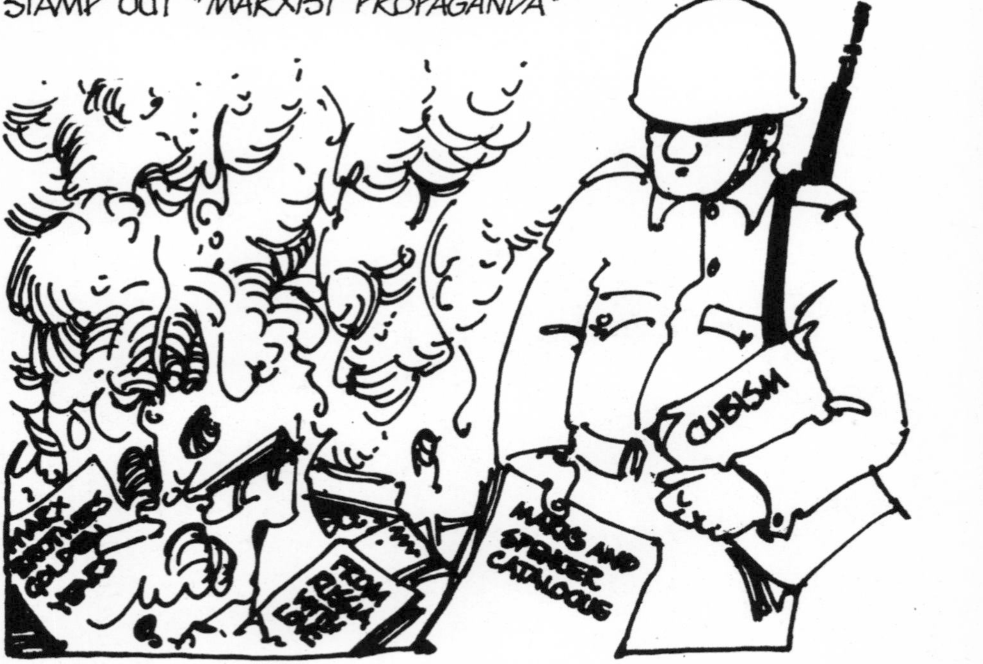

CUBISM

MUGS AND STEINER CATALOGUE

THE JUNTA HAS TRIED TO STAMP OUT THE WHOLE OF THE "POPULAR CULTURE" WHICH FLOURISHED UNDER POPULAR UNITY.

MANY POPULAR SONGS ARE BANNED

NAMES OF STREETS AND DISTRICTS WERE CHANGED.
USE OF THE TERM "COMPAÑERO" (COMRADE) WAS PROHIBITED

NEWSPAPERS, MAGAZINES, T.V., RADIO — ALL WERE THOROUGHLY PURGED, LEAVING ONLY THE RIGHT-WING MEDIA. EVEN THAT IS KEPT UNDER TIGHT CONTROL.

AN EXAMPLE FROM "DISNEY LANDIA" — SANTIAGO, MARCH 1974

FOREIGN JOURNALISTS WHO HAVE DARED TO REVEAL SOME OF WHAT IS GOING ON IN CHILE HAVE BEEN HARASSED, ARRESTED AND EXPELLED.

AFTER THE COUP, THE CHURCHES WERE VIRTUALLY THE ONLY LEGAL ORGANIZATIONS ABLE TO OFFER SOME HELP AND PROTECTION

■ THE **COMMITTEE FOR PEACE** WAS ESTABLISHED BY THE CATHOLIC AND OTHER CHURCHES. IT HELPED SET UP SOUP KITCHENS, COOPERATIVES ETC. AND PROVIDED LEGAL AND OTHER ASSISTANCE. ITS CAREFUL DOCUMENTATION OF "DISAPPEARED" PRISONERS, TORTURES, ILLEGAL ARRESTS, HARDSHIPS ETC. WAS BECOMING A THORN IN THE SIDE OF THE JUNTA

THE CHURCHES, DESPITE THEIR CAUTION AND INFLUENCE, HAVE COME UNDER INCREASING ATTACK

■ BISHOP HELMUT FRENZ, THEN HEAD OF CHILE'S LUTHERAN CHURCH, WAS EXPELLED FROM THE COUNTRY AS WERE A NUMBER OF OTHER CHURCH FIGURES
■ PROPAGANDA AND PHYSICAL ATTACKS AGAINST CRITICAL CHURCH FIGURES WERE STEPPED UP SHARPLY
■ IN LATE 1975 THE JUNTA CLOSED DOWN THE COMMIT--TEE FOR PEACE, ARRESTING AND TORTURING A NUMBER OF CHURCH PEOPLE, INCLUDING THE BRITISH DOCTOR SHEILA CASSIDY.

A NEW **VICARIATE OF SOLIDARITY**, A MORE LIMITED AND CAUTIOUS BODY, HAS BEEN SET UP BY THE CATHOLIC CHURCH

THE JUNTA HAS WORKED TO MAINTAIN A SHAM INSTITUTIONAL LEGALITY.

THUS THEY PROCLAIM THAT THEY HAVE STUCK SCRUPULOUSLY TO THE CONSTITUTIONAL DIVISION OF POWERS BETWEEN THE THREE BRANCHES OF GOVERNMENT....

SEPARATE REGIONAL AND LOCAL GOVERNMENT STRUCTURES HAVE BEEN MAINTAINED, BUT THEY WERE REORGANISED TO COINCIDE WITH MILITARY REGIONS AND THE APPROPRIATE MILITARY COMMANDER APPOINTED SIMULTANEOUSLY TO CIVILIAN OFFICE

OF COURSE, FLEXIBILITY IS CALLED FOR...

DECREE LAW Nº 788 STATES THAT, IN CASES WHERE A DECREE LAW CONTRADICTS THE CONSTITUTION, THE FORMER PREVAILS. **DECREE LAW Nº 521**, WHICH LEGALISES THE **DINA** (CHILE'S GESTAPO), HAS THREE *SECRET* ARTICLES.

THE JUNTA'S FOREIGN POLICIES HAVE BEEN AS SUBTLE AS ITS DOMESTIC POLICIES

IT WAS DECIDED TO DEVELOP MORE TIES WITH AFRICA WHERE, ACCORDING TO THE JUNTA, "THERE DOESN'T EXIST AN ADVANCED CONCIOUSNESS CONCERNING HUMAN RIGHTS."

MARIO ARNELLO, A JUNTA REPRESENTATIVE AT THE U.N. ASSEMBLY, STATED......

"THE AFRICAN LEADERS WHO MAKE INTERNATIONAL POLICY HAVE RECENTLY COME DOWN FROM THE PALM TREES"

ALL CRITICISM IS ATTACKED AS PART OF THE "WORLD COMMUNIST CONSPIRACY" AGAINST CHILE. EVEN THE U.S. AMBASSADOR IN CHILE HAS BEEN ATTACKED FOR HIS COMMUNIST LINKS! CHILE'S CIRCLE OF FRIENDS HAS BEEN REDUCED TO SUCH COUNTRIES AS SOUTH AFRICA AND SOUTH KOREA.

IN CHILE, POPULAR DISCONTENT HAS GROWN WIDER AND STRONGER — AND WITH IT ORGANISATION AND ACTS OF RESISTANCE HAVE ALSO GROWN — BECAUSE OF THIS THE JUNTA HAS FELT IT NECESSARY TO MAINTAIN A PERMANENT STATE OF SEIGE DESPITE THE VERY HIGH POLITICAL COSTS BOTH AT HOME AND ABROAD.

ALL THE LEFT PARTIES OPERATE IN CLAND-ESTINITY AND EACH CIRCULATES ITS OWN NEWSPAPER OR PUBLICATION (THESE ARE HAND-SIZED FOR EASY CONCEALMENT) DESPITE THE FACT THAT ANYONE CAUGHT WITH A COPY IS SUBJECT TO IMMEDIATE ARREST AND TORTURE — THE COMBINED CIRCULATION OF THESE IS EQUAL TO THAT OF CHILE'S LEADING WEEKLY (20,000)

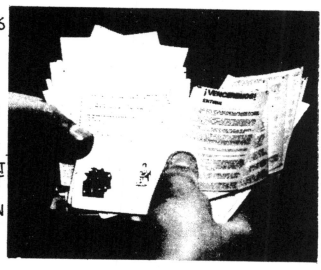

DENUNCIATIONS ARE FOLLOWED BY IMMEDIATE ARREST — THE LEFT RETALIATED BY HOAX DENUNCIATIONS OF THE RIGHT...

SORRY COLONEL — WE HAD A PHONE CALL ABOUT ILLEGAL ACTIVITIES GOING ON AT THIS ADDRESS..

... MUST BE ANOTHER OF THOSE HOAXES...

ALL OVER THE COUNTRY
CLANDESTINE "RESISTANCE
COMMITTEES" HAVE BEEN
SET UP

SLOGANS AND PARTY
SYMBOLS ARE CONSTANTLY
BEING PUT UP ON WALLS
AND OTHER PUBLIC
PLACES

PACKETS OF LEAFLETS ARE
PLACED ON HIGH BUILDINGS
IN SUCH A WAY THAT
THEY WILL BLOW OPEN
AND SCATTER AFTER
THOSE RESPONSIBLE
HAVE ESCAPED

MESSAGES ARE WRITTEN
ON BANKNOTES

RELIGIOUS EVENTS ARE USED TO DEMONSTRATE POPULAR FEELING
AND PARTY ORGANISATION — ALL THE PARTIES MOBILISED ON
24TH NOVEMBER 1974 (OFFICIALLY THE END OF THE CHILEAN
SAINTS' YEAR) FOR A MARCH — 500,000 PEOPLE JOINED
IN WITH BANNERS AND CHANTS THAT ONLY THINLY VEILED THE
ORIGINAL PARTY SLOGANS

(THE NEXT YEAR THE
MARCH WAS CALLED OFF)

OFFICIAL EVENTS ARE SOMETIMES MET WITH ORGANISED (BUT INNOCUOUSLY PRESENTED) BOYCOTTS...

A FORM OF RESISTANCE WIDELY PRACTICED, WHICH ALSO HELPS RELIEVE SOME OF THE POVERTY AND HARDSHIP CAUSED BY THE JUNTA, IS OVER-PACKING — PACKETS OF FOOD ETC. ARE FILLED WITH MORE THAN THE STATED CAPACITY — A SORT OF POSITIVE SABOTAGE!

ACTIVE TRADE UNION WORK IS CONTINUED ON AN ILLEGAL OR SEMI-LEGAL BASIS
  IN SOME PLACES STRIKES HAVE TAKEN PLACE - THERE WAS A SUCCESSFUL 20 MINUTE STRIKE AT CHUQUICAMATA COPPER MINE AND A SIMILAR STRIKE IN VALPARAISO'S PORT AREA DESPITE THE MASSIVE REPRESSION SUCH ACTION USUALY BRINGS

EVEN JUNTA-APPOINTED UNION OFFICIALS ARE FORCED TO START SPEAKING OUT SO AS NOT TO SEEM TOTALLY ISOLATED

THE JUNTA FAVOURS A SYSTEM WHERE THE OLDEST WORKERS ARE APPOINTED AS UNION OFFICIALS

MILITARY PERSONNEL – INCLUDING
TOP-RANKING OFFICERS – HAVE
BECOME INCREASINGLY
DISCONTENTED.

OVER 30 GENERALS HAVE BEEN
"RETIRED" IN LESS THAN 3 YEARS

THE CONSTITUTIONALIST GENERAL
CARLOS PRATS WAS SO FEARED
AS A POSSIBLE LEADER OF
DISSENTING FORCES THAT HE WAS
HUNTED DOWN IN ARGENTINA
(WHERE HE WAS LIVING IN EXILE)
AND KILLED, TOGETHER WITH HIS
WIFE

GENERAL **BONILLA**, THEN DEFENSE
MINISTER AND ANOTHER POSSIBLE
LEADER OF DISSENT, DIED IN A
MYSTERIOUS HELICOPTER "ACCIDENT"

THE JUNTA HAS COMPLAINED OF 'SUBVERSIVE ELEMENTS'
ACTIVE IN THE ARMED FORCES AND MANY OFFICERS AND SOLDIERS
HAVE BEEN REMOVED IN PURGES

AMONG THE DISENCHANTED
ARE THOSE WHO ORIGINALLY
SUPPORTED THE COUP –
SUCH AS EDUARDO FREI
AND HIS FOLLOWERS WITHIN
THE CHRISTIAN-DEMOCRATIC
PARTY, MANY HAVE BECOME
INCREASINGLY OUTSPOKEN
IN THEIR CRITICISM OF THE
JUNTA

¡VIVA LA DEMOCRACIA!

THE MIDDLE CLASSES (THE
PROFESSIONALS, THE SMALL
BUSINESSMEN AND TRADES
–MEN AND LANDOWNERS)
HAVE BEEN BADLY HIT BY
THE ECONOMIC CRISIS AND
BY THEIR LOSS OF FREEDOM.
THEY HAVE LESS AND LESS
FAITH IN THE JUNTA, AND
MORE AND MORE OF THEM
ARE LOOKING FOR A
DEMOCRATIC ALTERNATIVE.

THE LEFT HAS HAD TO FACE NOT ONLY THE FIERCE MILITARY REPRESSION BUT ALSO ITS OWN CONTINUED DISUNITY. THE MISTAKES AND DIVISIONS WHICH UNDERLAY THE SEPTEMBER DEFEAT (REFORMISM, ADVENTURISM, HESITATIONS, SECTARIANISM, AND BUREAUCRATISM) HAVE CONTINUED TO IMPEDE EFFECTIVE ACTION.

NEVERTHELESS, EVERYBODY IS IN AGREEMENT THAT **UNITY** IS ESSENTIAL TO BRING DOWN THE PINOCHET REGIME, AND THAT THE FORMATION OF A POLITICAL FRONT OF LEFT FORCES CANNOT BE POSTPONED....

FACED WITH GROWING POPULAR DISCONTENT, AND ITS OWN INABILITY TO REFORM AND OFFER ECONOMIC DEVELOPMENT. IMPERIALISM HAS BEEN IMPOSING A SYSTEM OF REACTIONARY MILITARY DOMINATION THROUGHOUT THE LATIN AMERICAN CONTINENT.

BRAZIL	1964
BOLIVIA	1971
URUGUAY	1973
CHILE	1973
ARGENTINA	1976

ONLY ONE THING STANDS IN THE WAY OF NEAT MILITARY UNIFORMITY BEING ESTABLISHED – THE DETERMINED RESISTANCE OF THE LATIN AMERICAN PEOPLE (WHO HAVE BECOME FOREIGNERS IN THEIR OWN LANDS) ....

DESPITE THE GROWING HARDSHIPS, LATIN AMERICANS ARE INCREASINGLY SHARING THE LESSONS OF THEIR EXPERIENCES AND WORKING TOGETHER TO FIGHT THE COMMON ENEMY

AFTER THE POPULIST MOVEMENT WAS SMASHED IN BRAZIL, WE TRIED URBAN GUERRILLA METHODS BUT REMAINED ISOLATED FROM THE PEOPLE

WE TRIED THE SAME THING IN URUGUAY, AS WELL AS A GENERAL STRIKE THAT LASTED NEARLY 15 DAYS BUT A GENERAL STRIKE IS NOT ENOUGH IN ITSELF

IN CHILE WE MADE TREMENDOUS ADVANCES UNDER DEMOCRATIC CONDITIONS, BUT WE WEREN'T PREPARED FOR VIOLENT CONFRONTATION

IN ARGENTINA WE HAVE LEARNED TO COMBINE MANY DIFFERENT FORMS OF STRUGGLE AND HAVE BUILT A POWERFUL WORKING CLASS MOVEMENT DESPITE 20 YEARS UNDER A VIRTUAL STATE OF SIEGE AND THE GROWING REPRESSION SINCE THE 1976 COUP

WE EACH HAVE OUR PROBLEMS AND WAYS OF SOLVING THEM, BUT LET'S REMEMBER CHE GUEVARA WHO WAS BORN IN ARGENTINA, FOUGHT IN CUBA AND DIED HEROICALLY IN BOLIVIA

OURS IS A CONTINENTAL STRUGGLE FOR SOCIALISM

91

THE CHILEAN PEOPLE HAVE BEEN FAR
FROM ISOLATED IN THEIR STRUGGLE....

FROM THE FIRST DAYS OF THE COUP A GREAT WAVE OF
SOLIDARITY EMERGED. - WORKERS ALL OVER THE WORLD
FELT THAT THE DEFEAT BEING SUFFERED BY THE CHILEAN
PEOPLE WAS ALSO THEIR DEFEAT, THAT AN ATTACK ON
WORKERS AND POPULAR FORCES 'ANYWHERE WAS AN
ATTACK ON THEM AS WELL

MANY STARTED BLACKING ACTIONS
ESPECIALLY AGAINST SHIPMENTS OF ARMS

CAMPAIGNS WERE SET UP THROUGHOUT THE
WORLD TO SUPPORT THE CHILEAN PEOPLE

HERE IN GREAT BRITAIN, THE **CHILE SOLIDARITY CAMPAIGN** (A UNITARIAN CAMPAIGN CONSISTING OF ALL THE BRITISH LEFT-WING PARTIES) WAS SET UP TO DIRECT SOLIDARITY WORK

IT HAS HELPED PROMOTE ACTIONS TO WEAKEN AND ISOLATE THE DICTATORSHIP AS WELL AS PROVIDE MATERIAL AND OTHER SUPPORT TO THE POPULAR RESISTANCE. - ACTION AND ORGANISATION HAVE CONTINUED TO GROW, TO THE POINT WHERE THE CAMPAIGN NOW ENJOYS THE SUPPORT OF 66 LOCAL COMMITTEES AND OVER 100 AFFILIATED ORGANIZATIONS INCLUDING THE FOLLOWING TRADE UNIONS AT A NATIONAL LEVEL:

ACTT ASLEF ASTMS AUEW AUEW-TASS FTAT G&MWU NATSOPA NUM NUPE NUR NUSeamen NUSheet Metal Workers NUGSAT NUTGW POEU SLADE SOGAT Tobacco Workers Union T&GWU*

* not formally affiliated, but officially represented on CSC Executive Committee.

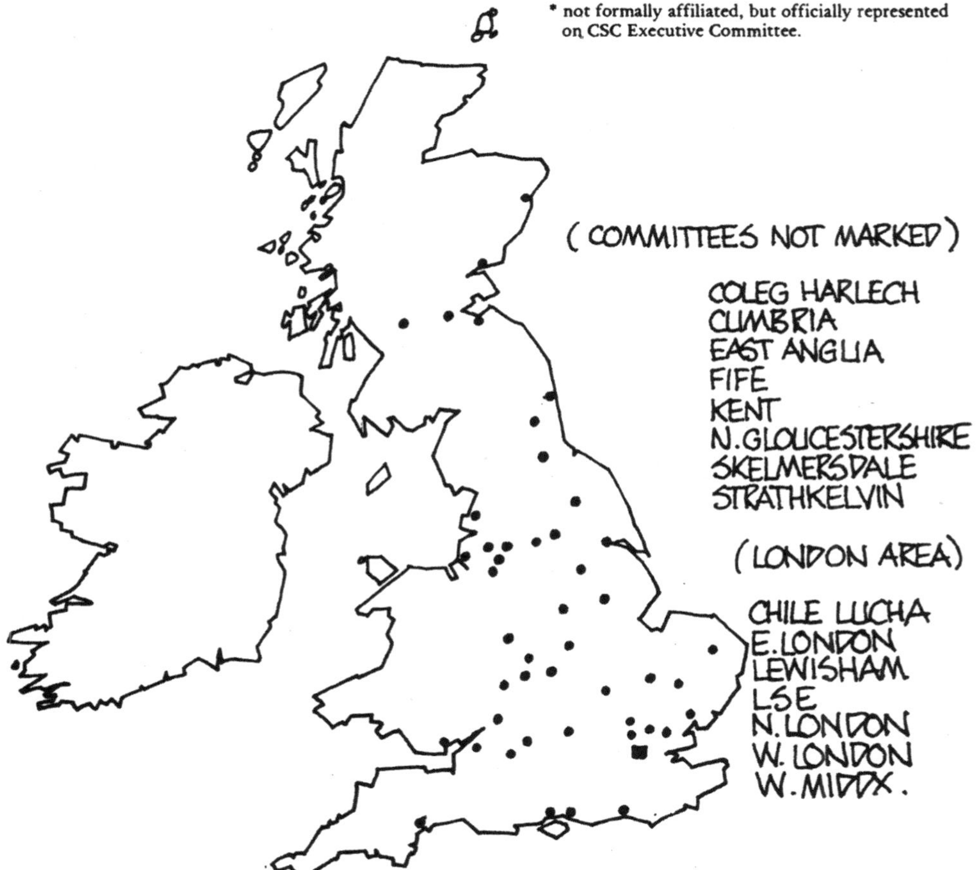

(COMMITTEES NOT MARKED)

COLEG HARLECH
CUMBRIA
EAST ANGLIA
FIFE
KENT
N. GLOUCESTERSHIRE
SKELMERSDALE
STRATHKELVIN

(LONDON AREA)

CHILE LUCHA
E. LONDON
LEWISHAM
LSE
N. LONDON
W. LONDON
W. MIDDX.

Blacking

IN OCTOBER 1973 LIVERPOOL DOCKERS HEARD OF THE KILLING OF GUILLERMO (A VALPARAISO DOCKER WHO HAD VISITED THEM DURING POPULAR UNITY).

IN THE SAME MONTH DOCKERS STARTED BOYCOTTS AGAINST THE CHILEAN JUNTA.

A Santiago evening newspaper of 13th November 1973 carrying the headline — "THE BOYCOTT AGAINST CHILE HAS STARTED — ENGLISH DOCKERS REFUSE TO UNLOAD CARGO".

THE EFFECT IN CHILE HAS BEEN ENORMOUS, BOOSTING WORKERS' MORAL, DISRUPTING THE JUNTA'S PLANS AND SHAKING THE CONFIDENCE OF THEIR SUPPORTERS, AS WELL AS CAUSING GREAT MATERIAL LOSSES TO THE REGIME.

THE IDEA CAUGHT ON....

- ■ SEPTEMBER 1975 - **NUS** INSTRUCTS BRITISH SEAMEN NOT TO SAIL ON SHIPS CALLING AT CHILEAN PORTS.
- ■ 600 UNEMPLOYED SEAMEN IN LIVERPOOL REFUSE TO SIGN UP ON P.S.N.C. SHIPS.
- ■ **NUR** CRANE DRIVERS AT NEWHAVEN DOCKS REFUSE TO UNLOAD CHILEAN ONIONS – CARGO ROTS.
- ■ **STUC** AND **TUC** MAKE OFFICIAL CONSUMER BOYCOTT OF CHILEAN WINE.
- ■ **BMC** REFUSE TO ALLOW EXPORT OF SPARES AND COMPONENTS TO BRITISH LEYLAND FACTORY IN CHILE.
- ■ **ICI** NORTHWICH WORKERS RESOLVE TO PRODUCE NOTHING MORE FOR CHILE.
- ■ **ITF** ORDERS AFFILIATES TO COMMENCE SYSTEMATIC HARASSMENT OF CHILEAN TRANSPORT FROM JANUARY 1ST 1976.
- ■ PORT WORKERS AT ROSYTH REFUSE TO SERVICE CHILEAN FRIGATE.

don't keep
Fascists
in business

don't buy
Chilean
shoes

Chile Solidarity Campai[gn]

'THE CHILEAN PEOPLE ASK'
STOP THE SUBS

IN 1975 THE BRITISH GOVERNMENT REFUSED TO RENEGOTIATE THE CHILEAN DEBT. (CHILE OWES GREAT BRITAIN ABOUT £120,000,000 OF WHICH £15,000,000 WAS DUE THAT YEAR) THIS CAUSED SERIOUS TROUBLE FOR THE JUNTA.

IT IS THOUGHT THAT UP TO 300,000 CHILEANS HAVE BEEN FORCED TO SEEK REFUGE IN OTHER COUNTRIES – THE LARGE MAJORITY OF THEM HAVE TRIED TO STAY IN NEIGHBOURING ARGENTINA.

INTERNATIONALLY, THE SOLIDARITY CAMPAIGNS, THROUGH ADOPTION SCHEMES AND OTHER PRESSURES, HAVE FORCED THE JUNTA TO RELEASE AT LEAST SOME OF ITS PRISONERS TO GO INTO EXILE

IN BRITAIN, AS IN MOST COUNTRIES, A SPECIAL REFUGEE PROGRAMME WAS SET UP AND SO FAR, SOME 1700 CHILEANS HAVE ARRIVED.

FOR SOME IT IS THE END OF A LONG TRAIL OF FLIGHT THROUGH SEVERAL LATIN-AMERICAN COUNTRIES ....

ONCE IN BRITAIN, THE REFUGEES ARE TAKEN CARE OF BY THE LOCAL CHILE COMMITTEES AND THE LOCAL COMMUNITY WHO HELP THEM FIND HOUSING, JOBS, ENGLISH LESSONS AND FRIENDS - THERE REMAINS THE HOPE THAT IN THE FUTURE THEY WILL BE ABLE TO RETURN HOME TO CHILE

WITH THE COUP IN ARGENTINA, HALF A MILLION FOREIGN REFUGEES FROM CHILE, BOLIVIA, URUGUAY, PARAGUAY AND BRAZIL ARE TRAPPED WITH NOWHERE ELSE LEFT TO GO IN SOUTH AMERICA

THE CAMPAIGN TO DEFEND HUMAN RIGHTS IN CHILE HAS SPREAD THROUGHOUT THE WORLD.

COMMISSIONS FROM THE INTERNATIONAL LABOUR ORGANIZATION, THE ORGANIZATION OF AMERICAN STATES, AMNESTY INTERNATIONAL, THE INTERNATIONAL COMMISSION OF DEMOCRATIC JURISTS, THE U.S. DEMOCRATIC PARTY, ETC. HAVE CARRIED OUT INVESTIGATIONS AND DENOUNCED THE TERRORIST STATE WHICH HAS BEEN IMPOSED UPON THE CHILEAN PEOPLE.

NEW BLANKET?? — THERE MUST BE ONE OF THOSE VISITING COMMISSIONS COMING

IN THE U.K, THE **CHILE COMMITTEE FOR HUMAN RIGHTS**, IN ADDITION TO A PRISONER ADOPTION PROGRAMME, GIVES SUPPORT TO SOUP KITCHENS AND OTHER PROJECTS SET UP TO HELP THE CHILEAN PEOPLE SURVIVE THE PRESENT REGIME

ONCE UPON A TIME THERE WAS TEA, SUGAR, FLOUR, RICE, POTATOES, MEAT, COFFEE....

SOME **2,000** PEOPLE PICKED UP BY THE JUNTA HAVE SIMPLY "DISAPPEARED" AND MORE ARE "DISAPPEARING" EVERY DAY

HUNDREDS OF SWORN TESTIMONIES FROM WITNESSES TO THESE ARRESTS HAVE BEEN SUBMITTED TO THE SUPREME COURT AND OTHER BODIES, BUT TO NO AVAIL

WILL YOU STOP INSISTING ON THIS RIDICULOUS STORY OF YOUR HUSBAND'S ARREST — MOST PROBABLY HE'S ABANDONED YOU FOR ANOTHER WOMAN

AN INTERNATIONAL CAMPAIGN HAS BEEN LAUNCHED TO FORCE THE JUNTA TO REVEAL WHAT HAS HAPPENED TO THESE PRISONERS

IN MAY 1974, THE FOLLOWING COMMUNIQUE WAS RECEIVED FROM THE CHILEAN UNDERGROUND NEWS AGENCY "**RESISTENCIA**"....

"THE HAWKER HUNTER PLANES, WHICH WERE RECENTLY BOUGHT IN GREAT BRITAIN AND ARRIVED TWO MONTHS AGO, HAVE BEEN SABOTAGED AT THE MILITARY AIRPORT OF "EL BOSQUE" NEAR SANTIAGO. SAND AND OTHER SUBSTANCES HAVE BEEN ADDED TO THE FUEL SO THAT THE ENGINES WERE RUINED"

MEANWHILE, WORKERS AT ROLLS-ROYCE FACTORIES IN EAST KILBRIDE PREVENTED EIGHT REMAINING ENGINES FROM LEAVING BRITAIN — (IT WAS HAWKER-HUNTERS WHICH WERE USED TO BOMB THE MONEDA PALACE IN 1973.)

AS A CONSEQUENCE OF THE COMBINED ACTION OF BRITISH WORKERS AND THE UNDERGROUND WORK OF THE RESISTANCE, THE CHILEAN AIRFORCE HAS BEEN FORCED TO CUT ITS FLIGHTS BY HALF.

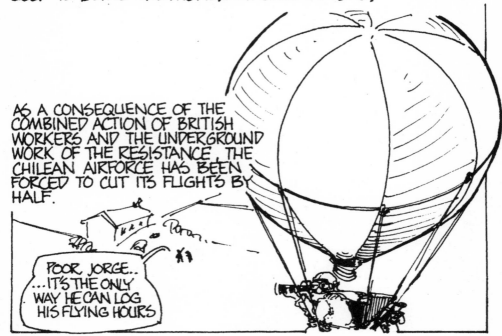

100

ONE ENEMY... ONE STRUGGLE

DON'T THEY EVER GIVE UP?!

ONCE AGAIN, THE OLD BANNER IS RAISED. ONCE AGAIN THERE IS A COMMON STRUGGLE AGAINST FOREIGN EXPLOITATION AND DOMINATION. — BEFORE, THE ENEMY WAS SPANISH COLONIAL RULE, AND THE STRUGGLE WAS THAT OF THE LATIN AMERICANS TO FREE THEMSELVES FROM THIS YOKE

— TODAY THE MULTINATIONALS STAND AT THE HEAD OF THE ENEMY'S RANKS, FOLLOWED BY A RETINUE OF INTELLIGENCE AGENCIES, FINANCIAL BODIES, COMPANIES, GOVERNMENTS AND OTHERS WHOSE AIM IS TO EXTRACT EVER GREATER PROFITS AT THE EXPENSE OF THE PEOPLE AND KEEP THE SYSTEM GOING.

NOT ONLY THE PEOPLE OF LATIN AMERICA, BUT WORKERS AND PEOPLE THROUGHOUT THE WORLD ARE THREATENED BY THESE FORCES

CHILE'S PEOPLE STRUGGLE NOW TO BUILD A TRULY DEMOCRATIC SOCIALIST SOCIETY — IT WILL TAKE A LONG TIME AND THEY WILL NEED HELP FROM ALL THOSE WHO SUPPORT THEM EVERYWHERE — BUT IN THE END THEY KNOW THAT VICTORY WILL BE THEIRS.

A PEOPLE UNITED WILL NEVER BE DEFEATED! VENCEREMOS!

CHRIS WELCH HAS DONE THE DRAWINGS AND ARTWORK FOR THIS BOOK. HE HAS WORKED IN COMICS SINCE 1971 AND IN VARIOUS GRAPHIC MEDIA SINCE 1965.

CARTOONS BY OTHER ARTISTS HAVE ALSO BEEN USED – CREDITS HAVE BEEN GIVEN WHERE POSSIBLE – WE OFFER OUR THANKS TO ALL OF THEM.

THE TEXT HAS BEEN WRITTEN COLLECTIVELY UNDER THE GENERAL DIRECTION OF LARRY WRIGHT AND A. MAGO. WE THANK CHILE LUCHA, A LOCAL COMMITTEE OF THE CHILE SOLIDARITY CAMPAIGN, FOR ITS INVALUABLE HELP IN THE PRODUCTION AND CONTENTS OF THIS BOOK. ALSO THANKS TO GEOFF ROWLEY FOR HIS WORK IN THE EARLY PARTS

INTRODUCTION TO CHILE

PRODUCED AND PUBLISHED BY BOLIVAR PUBLICATIONS 10, RODERICK ROAD LONDON NW3 2NL

USEFUL ADDRESSES:

CHILE SOLIDARITY CAMPAIGN
129, SEVEN SISTERS ROAD – LONDON N7 – 01·272 4299
CHILE COMMITTEE FOR HUMAN RIGHTS
1, CAMBRIDGE TERRACE – LONDON NW1 – 01·935 5953
CONTEMPORARY ARCHIVE ON LATIN AMERICA
1, CAMBRIDGE TERRACE – LONDON NW1 – 01·487 5277
JOINT WORKING GROUP FOR REFUGEES FROM CHILE IN BRITAIN
446, UXBRIDGE ROAD – LONDON W12 – 01·749 5851/5865

USEFUL READINGS:

NEW CHILE – (NORTH AMERICAN CONGRESS ON LATIN AMERICA, IN DEPTH ANALYSIS OF CHILE UP TO POPULAR UNITY
CHILE MONITOR – (REGULAR INFORMATION ANALYSIS; FROM C.S.C.)
CHILE FIGHTS – (AGITATIONAL MAGAZINE OF THE C.S.C.)
ITT DOCUMENTS – (SPOKESMAN BOOKS 1972)
LATIN AMERICA/LATIN AMERICA ECONOMIC REPORT (AUTHORITATIVE WEEKLY NEWS MAGAZINES ON LATIN AMERICA, PUBLISHED IN LONDON)

L.C.P. (T.U.) Ltd.—56869